PRAISE FC

MW00855949

"Kathleen McIntyre's *The Nat* practical guidebook written for anyone looking to come home to a deeper sense of connection with themselves and life itself. She guides the reader to feel and know their own body as a trustworthy inner guide to connecting with Nature through sensory exercises that can be done anywhere. As McIntyre says, "Nature will meet you exactly where you are" and "help you reclaim your purpose and passion for life, your sense of self-worth and vitality." I have lived, written and taught about embodiment and reconnection with (our true) Nature as a path home for many years, and welcome *The Nature Reset* as a detailed map that reveals true practices for awakening harmony in ourselves, and for bringing more peace into the world. **"**

—**Robin Rose Bennett,** author of Healing Magic,
The Gift of Healing Herbs, A Green Witch's Pocketbook of Wisdom,
and A Young Green Witch's Guide to Plant Magic

"Wonderment is seeing the familiar in unfamiliar ways. Reading this book left me in wonderment about my relationship to the natural world that surrounds me. The Nature Reset shows how connecting with nature—in the many micro and macro-dosing manners clearly discussed—can help us to re-connect with our authentic selves and counter the hurry sickness that has become the norm of our times.

Kathleen guides the reader through a multi-sensory experience while gently offering her direction, wisdom, and encouragement as she teaches how connecting with nature can be a pleasure-filled pathway to accessing the best evidence-based approaches to restoring and sustaining wellbeing, resilience, and authentic self-compassion. **"**

—**Wayne M. Sotile,** Ph.D., Founder Sotile Center for Resilience

"Kathleen writes directly to the heart as if she is your most beloved friend. She writes with such compassion for the human experience that you feel she is right next to you, holding your hand on the journey to experience your true self. **"**

—**Jennifer Jakubecy,** Ph.D., Executive Director, Davidson Green School

"Kathleen's book is a kind and encouraging guide for any age to help restore our connections with Nature. Climate change is a concerning reality. But Kathleen helps us find mindfulness, solace, balance, and endurance through her intelligent practices for Nature resetting."

—**Clare Walker Leslie**, author of A Year In Nature: A Memoir of Solace

"The Nature Reset contains a true map to help you find your way home (to yourself!). In this field guide, you'll wander with purpose out in nature, noticing your body, your breath, and Nature herself. This guide gently weaves together scientific insights and practical advice to highlight the profound impacts of nature on your nervous system, body, and spirit. I especially loved pages 98-101, which offer an "at a glance" set of nature reset practices to incorporate into your life. The foundation message: go outside often! And don't forget to take this incredibly useful field guide with you as your companion!

—**Angie Stegall**, ANFT Certified Forest Therapy Guide & Martha Beck Certified Wayfinder Life Coach

"In her debut book, *The Nature Reset*, Kathleen McIntyre generously shares her experiences moving from a disembodied, anxious life into a whole, serene self–using Nature as her guide. This book challenges the reader to practice the lessons prescribed rather than just assimilate them mentally. This is not a book about learning; it is a book about trying. A field guide, it leads the reader into a mindful relationship with Nature that can both renew and restore physical, mental and spiritual health. As McIntyre notes, you don't have to be in the middle of the woods to get something out of this book. Meet Nature where you are and let her change you for the better."

—**Hope Andersen**, author of How to Remodel a Life

# THE NATURE RESET

# THE NATURE RESET

**restore** your nervous system

**reclaim** your body

**reawaken** your spirit

A Practical Guide

KATHLEEN McINTYRE

Cover and book design by Erica De Flamand
Illustrations by Erica De Flamand

Library of Congress Cataloging-in-Publication Data

Names: McIntyre, Kathleen, author
Title: The Nature Reset: A Practical Guide to Restore Your Nervous System, Reclaim Your Body, and Reawaken Your Spirit Wherever You Are / Kathleen McIntyre
Description: Davidson, NC : NatureSoma Press, [2024] | Includes bibliographical references. |
Summary: A practical guide to accessing the therapeutic benefits of nature within the urban, suburban, and wilderness landscape through mindfulness, embodiment, and nature connection practices.
Identifiers: LCCN 2024901245 (print) | ISBN 979-8-9897581-0-4 (paperback) | ISBN 979-8-9897581-1-1 (ebook)
Subjects: LCSH: Nature–Psychological aspects. | Mind and body therapies. | Nature, Healing power. | Well-being. | Self-help. | Self-realization.
Classification: LCC BF353.5.N37 2024 (print) | DDC 155.9–dc23

First printing, March 2024
ISBN 979-8-9897581-0-4
Ebook ISBN 979-8-9897581-1-1
Printed in the United States of America

Published by NatureSoma Press
99 Jackson St. Unit 1246
Davidson, NC 28036

# DEDICATION

This book is dedicated to the memory of
Roy Alexander, first executive director
of the Davidson Lands Conservancy
and lifelong educator.

He touched the heart of every person
who crossed his path and blessed
the earth with each step he took.

Roy was a bridge between two worlds.

# NAVIGATION

# FOUNDATIONS

# come home to your body

Within the core of your being resides a point of balance. It is always there, just below the layers of accumulated stress, worries, feelings of not-enoughness, or over-efforting. When you settle into this balance point, your heart, mind, and body come into coherence—you experience states of authenticity, peace, and flow. This feels like home. Many of us have been searching far and wide for those elusive ruby slippers to take us home, but they have been with us all along. This book is about resetting your course to home from wherever you find yourself.

Fortunately, finding your point of balance is within reach. It begins by feeling at home within your body—that unconditional, deep down feeling that you are safe and all is well. Despite how often we struggle to feel at home in our bodies and the world, the body is where we experience true inner peace. How do we reconcile this? How can we "be in the moment," at home in our bodies, amidst the external and internal whirlwinds that seem to cast us off course?

If you can relate to these questions, you are not alone. There are many origins of this disconnect in today's world. For some, it traces back to childhood—to moments of emotional overload, traumatic experiences, or not feeling seen and heard. Your biology responded by disconnecting—a kind of emotional detachment from the body—as a means of protection.

As these experiences carried into adulthood, coupled with stress that exceeds one's adaptive ability, it is understandable how feeling at home within the body can be elusive. In turn, this may hamper your ability to connect meaningfully with the world around you.

Familiar as disconnection may feel, you also carry within you experiences and feelings of connection and belonging. Threads of peace, calm, and contentment have been woven through your life, offering you a sense of home and the desire to reside there more often. This book is a roadmap—a field guide—to that place. It is designed to clear the path and share the practical skills that can always lead you home.

How will we get there? This book is unique in that it is not about your mind; it is about your body. So, there are a few worn paths we won't be taking. We won't access home from our memories. We won't think, figure out, or cajole our way back to our home. We won't regress or imagine our way to it either. Although, at some point, we have all disconnected from the body in favor of the mind, this book is about learning how to do the opposite. The path home is through the body.

Does this sound difficult? Maybe even counterintuitive? That's why we are going to invite a trusted guide to take us there. And that guide is Nature. Each journey is different, but the power of Nature as your guide is universal. And Nature can be found everywhere. You will be amazed as you discover just how much you are already connected to the web-of-life and the healing strength of Nature.

Of course, one of the hallmarks of our modern age is our complicated relationship with Nature. There is no need for me to list the many ways we as humans are stressing the earth in catastrophic ways. But despite all we do as a species to cause harm, intentionally or unintentionally, Nature still calls us back, open-armed, with unconditional love.

Nature is always there to remind us of our resilience and wholeness, to remind us how to live well, and to remind us how to experience the present moment fully.

Healing through exposure to Nature is not a crutch or a gimmick; it is a return to who you actually are. As the late Theodore Roszak, who coined the term ecopsychology, wrote, "At its deepest level, the psyche remains sympathetically bonded to the earth that mothered us into existence."[1] This statement points a way back to the wisdom passed down through generations of people who lived close to the land. The earth is the primordial mother; her waters, minerals, and elements flow through our veins and make up our bones.

When I lead groups, I often ask participants to introduce themselves and share the landscape that lights them up or feels like home. Without hesitation, they know. Within this landscape, they feel held, nourished, restored, and enlivened. There is a bond that exists beyond what our rational mind can explain, not unlike a healthy bond between mother and child. This guide aims to expand and strengthen that bond.

My research as a scientist was in land reclamation, and these days, a lot of what I do with my Nature therapy clients mirrors that process. As with drastically disturbed land, the challenges of life can leave many of us feeling internally barren or numb, lacking vitality and creativity, and feeling devoid of life's beauty and richness. There are similar broad strokes to both the reclamation of land and the inner landscape of humans. These involve deep nourishment, connection, and rest. I have seen both land and hearts come back to life in astonishingly short order under such care. A key part of our reclamation journey happens through connection with Nature.

The practices I share will support you in connecting with Nature in ways that help you reclaim your purpose and passion for life, your sense of self-worth, your vitality, and your enoughness.

This guide will help you to see Nature as a powerful ally. Not just as in, "Oh, this is a nice place to take a vacation." But as in, "Oh my gosh, my mental health really depends upon this tree, this water, this experience."

Don't worry—you don't have to live in the woods in order to use this book! You don't even have to have a lot of free time. Whether you are a business professional living in the heart of a city, a new parent, or recently retired, Nature will meet you exactly where you are. Each time the outer landscape dances with your inner landscape, rhythms will align. As you embark on this journey, you will feel a growing ability to settle inward and reconnect with your body. Reset to this solid foundation, and you will discover new paths of vitality, purpose, and connection with family, friends, community, and Nature.

**This is the journey home.**

For additional resources and audio recordings, visit naturesoma.com/reset.

CHAPTER 1

# how do i know this to be true?

Nature and I go way back. One of my earliest memories of feeling held by Nature and the sense of home she instilled is from the early 1980s. I was on my old metal swing, my pigtails flying, sporting leg warmers. A cool breeze blew across my face, swirling the multicolored leaves on the ground and bringing with it the distinct smell of fall in the air. At that moment, I had a spontaneous sense of awe, peace, and relaxation. That was when I fell in love with Nature. I was home.

From that moment on, Nature became my refuge in a complicated world. I spent as much time outside as I possibly could. Nature gave me feelings of freedom, joy, and peacefulness. Later in life, I stumbled upon the teachings of people who lived close to the earth and found that they described what I felt—a reverence for the land and a reverence for our connection with it. In that wisdom from the Americas, Africa, and my lineage, the Celts, I felt that I had found my community and anchor.

Despite the bond that I had with the natural world, my nervous system showed signs of dysregulation as a child, although in that era it went unrecognized. I never slept, was highly sensitive to others' emotions, felt a low-level internal restlessness, and had an incredibly hard time focusing and being organized. But I was a really nice kid and always floated by.

I don't even think I had heard of the word anxiety until I went off to college—yet it had probably been a companion since birth.

As I got older, I became acutely aware of habitat loss, pollution, famines, and poor agricultural practices destroying the land— crises not on many young people's radar back in the early nineties. I began feeling devastated and angry, which fed into the anxiety lingering right below the surface. Those of you who are currently in despair about the environmental crisis we are in, I hear you. And the pathway through this type of despair is action.

Back then, my action step to be part of the solution was mastering an academic perspective on the impact of humans on the environment and how these choices affect human health. I received a B.S. in Environmental Health Science from the University of Georgia and then a Master's degree in Forestry Resources focused on land reclamation.

When I was in graduate school, I began leading women on adventures in the woods. We went backpacking, canoeing, and sea kayaking. But even as a leader in helping other people connect with Nature, my low-level anxiety was on the rise. I didn't know it at the time, but in the midst of my outdoorsy lifestyle, accumulated stress was disconnecting me from my body. Slowly and over time, I was losing my way home. Being out in Nature wasn't enough.

Outwardly, I seemed pretty laid back and fun-loving, but my nervous system told a different story. What story was playing out in my body? It was a feeling of floating, not settled, spinning at times, a panic feeling driving on highways at night, or rising up out of the blue. Decades of undiagnosed anxiety and searching for an elusive sense of inner peace went by.

Then one day, when I was living on the side of a mountain in Western North Carolina, feeling particularly unsettled, I went outside to sit by a massive oak tree in my yard. At that moment, I had a very strange realization: I felt witnessed and held by this tree. I knew that this old tree was offering me support, and I found myself going to her for comfort again and again when I was struggling. My relationship with Nature moved from the head to the heart, and I could feel this subtle shift in my body. It was something I couldn't unsee—it couldn't be unfelt. That awareness was like a homecoming. Since the only help modern medicine could offer me was medication, I suspended judgment and decided to see what I could learn from this sweet old oak tree.

Almost twenty years have passed since that encounter with the oak on the mountain, which was the embarkation point for a long journey of exploring Nature as a pathway toward peace in my own body. I felt like a detective—following different rabbit holes, figuring out what worked and what didn't. It was a long process. But through many years of commitment and paying close attention to my body and the natural world, I got to the place where I truly felt at home again. Ever since then, my passion has been to support others to feel at home in their bodies through connection with Nature.

## Nature Quantified – What the Research Says

Since the 1970s, researchers from around the world have been trying to quantify the benefits of Nature. What have they found out? The same thing that humans have experienced through the ages—Nature's restorative effects help to mitigate and prevent stress and mental fatigue. A thirty-minute visit to your local green or blue space brings a host of benefits, which include a decrease in stress hormone production, blood pressure, anxiety, and depression.[1,2] If you live in an area with greater bird abundance and vegetation cover, you are likely to be happier than those with less. Even taking a break from work and looking out a window can restore cognitive function.

In each of these situations, there is a change in your internal state for the better. Exposure to Nature has been one of the most underutilized yet free and most easily accessible forms of medicine in the West. Fortunately, due to the rigorous data collected in Japan on forest bathing, doctors there write "prescriptions" for time in Nature as part of their treatment plans. In many cases, a prescription for Nature is enough to decrease anxiety, depression, and the harmful effects of excess stress on the body, completely bypassing the need for prescription allopathic medicine.[3]

## Nature and the Missing Peace

At this point, you might be wondering, "If so much of her life was spent out in Nature, why did she still have anxiety?" First, I cannot imagine what my mental health would have been like without Nature! The regular doses of Nature helped me to keep creating, exploring, and living life. Yet, there was a sense of peace that perpetually eluded me.

While living in Manhattan in the early 2000s, I had the opportunity for a weekend retreat at the Omega Institute to hear Jon Kabat-Zinn and Daniel Siegel speak on mindfulness. One of my favorite and most succinct definitions of mindfulness is from Jon Kabat-Zinn, "paying attention in a particular way: on purpose, in the present moment, and non-judgmentally."[4] During this weekend, I discovered for the first time the missing peace.

I had started incorporating mindfulness practices into my life while living on the mountain, but listening and practicing with these two extraordinary leaders in the world of mindfulness was game-changing. And it wasn't just the impact of their gentleness, brilliance, and being in the presence of those who have practiced for many years—it was also the setting.

The Omega Institute was beautiful and serene—a great contrast to my city street in NYC. That weekend felt like a divine convergence. From that moment onward, I began to fuse my Nature practice with my mindfulness practice and discovered a new level of restoration for my nervous system.

Seeds planted within me from the oak tree I left behind on the mountain began to take root in a new way. With this growth, came more fertile ground and new teachers. The next piece of the puzzle came to me through Doug Silsbee, founder of Presence-Based Coaching and a beloved teacher. What I learned from Doug was key—he taught me embodiment. Embodiment to me is the felt sense of having a body. In addition, he taught me a new understanding of trauma, which affects our ability to be at home in our bodies, and offered me an awareness of the unexplored trauma within my own body.

Mindfulness and embodiment practices were the crux discoveries that allowed me to profoundly connect with my body and the natural world. It is the alchemy of combining Nature, mindfulness, and embodiment that creates healing, and it changed my life. The sum of these is greater than each part. Inner peace no longer eludes me, and the anxiety which was my baseline for years is only a memory. Yes, this was something I wanted to shout from the mountain tops, "I've found the missing peace!" And where else to first share the message than with that child on the swing? Sharing this magic with children seemed the perfect place to begin.

## Bringing it All Together

After leaving New York City, my family made its way to Davidson, North Carolina. It is here that, in 2013, I co-founded the Davidson Green School, a school that is anchored in nurturing the whole child, sustainability, and community action.

Mindfulness and Nature connection are hallmarks of its programming. One day I was facilitating a day-long Nature-based mindfulness outing for our youngest group of children, accompanied by their parents. I noticed that although the children were fine, the adults seemed to be in a heightened state when they arrived. They'd all rushed to get their kids there on time, left behind a long list of things to do, and each one seemed a little flustered. Their energy was way up.

Hours later, when we were walking back to the cars, I had a revelation: the parents had energetically shifted. Their minds had settled, their bodies had settled, and their spirits had settled. I hadn't really been noticing the parents during the day; I was focused on the students. The shift that happened within the adults was palpable; many commented on how relaxed and centered they felt. I was asked if I could lead the same experience for other adults. From that moment on, I've been developing programming and curricula for adults and children on Nature-based mindfulness.

Over the years, I have been amazed at the ability of adults to transform through developing a relationship with Nature and their bodies. Children are often more innately close to Nature, but with adults, there's a level of reawakening that astounds me. As adults, we separate ourselves more from the natural world and accumulate layers of stress, trauma, or both that can get in our way.

After a one-day Nature-based Mindfulness retreat, participants leave actually looking different, seemingly lighter. Some of the layers have unfurled or been integrated. I have seen it work so many times. How could I not share this knowledge, this pathway, with as many people as possible? Witnessing Nature's consistent positive impact on mental health and well-being inspired me to earn a Master's Degree in Clinical Social Work in order to speak with more authority on the relationship between mental health and Nature and the importance of access to both, for all. This is my journey and the "why" behind writing this field guide. It's my honor to share with you the results of years of synthesizing ideas, experiences, and processes to support you on your journey—a journey of connecting with Nature and your body to significantly enhance your mental, emotional, spiritual, and physical well-being.

## How to Use This Field Guide

I have always loved field guides. From identifying trees as a newbie graduate student in Forestry to foraging for wild edibles, field guides have always been in my pocket, in my backpack, and more recently on my phone.

A classic field guide would introduce you to the natural world visually, helping you to identify species, rocks, minerals, and soil types. However, this book is not about describing Nature to you, it is about *experiencing* Nature and allowing her to describe you. With the support of this field guide, Nature will show you how to reclaim a relationship with all parts of yourself, and with the natural world around you. You will consciously connect rather than spectate.

**I can't stress enough that this field guide is not for learning things; it is for trying things.**

To be clear, the lessons from Nature and practices in this book are not my teachings; they are both no one's and everyone's teachings. Within these pages are lessons of the natural world, learned by listening closely, observing her rhythms, and reclaiming the language of subtlety. Anchored in science but nourished and brought to life by the natural world, this field guide rests on the shoulders of generations who have walked gently on the earth, been in right relationship with her, and shared her story.

Despite all the research on Nature's restorative benefits, many of the mechanisms behind this enhanced well-being remain a mystery. Accepting this mystery and working with it will be part of the healing processes described in this book. As you move through the exercises, it is my belief that you will find your own healing in Nature and witness the change within your own life as the best and only proof of Nature's efficacy that you need.

The practices and lessons in this guide can be applied indoors, outdoors in wild spaces on your back porch, and everywhere in between. You can begin right where you are. They will restore and nourish you physically, mentally, emotionally, and spiritually. I will show you how to implement these practices into your everyday routine, resulting in sustainable change over time. And as with all field guides, this one is meant to get dirty, wrinkled, and shared.

For many of you, section one will be a remembrance, an "aha... yes." You might be introduced to new ways of thinking. Section one is designed to support, build a foundation, and inspire you as you experience the practices in section two. Section one will stimulate your mind, but it is the practices themselves that are the transformative elements of this guide. Feel free to skip about as you would with a field guide. If you are feeling the call to get right into the practices, just be sure you begin in chapter five with the foundational Body Practice and Heart Practice. Both of those practices support all of section two.

I am excited for you to begin!

CHAPTER 2

# the problem

I was twenty-two years old, sitting on a 14,000-foot peak in the wilderness of Colorado, surrounded by sheer beauty. But I felt nothing.

I'd just hiked from Denver to Durango, through some of the most pristine, most beautiful wilderness in our country. But when I got to the top of one of the highest mountains, I found that I didn't feel it. I couldn't feel it. I was in the midst of immense beauty, but it wasn't touching me. It was just... kind of good, and that was it. I remember thinking, "What is so wrong with me that I cannot feel this?" It made me very sad. In fact, I felt despair.

Obviously, I wanted nothing more than to experience the bliss and joy of the moment on that mountain peak. But I couldn't access it because I didn't know how to access my body. Gradually, through many years of accumulated stress, I had begun living entirely in my head, and my body had lost the ability to truly respond.

Recall a moment when you have felt a distinct disconnect. When you're disconnected, you feel like life is passing you by. You feel closed off—not able to reach across the void created by disconnection. You can walk through the woods and have nothing but static in your mind, static in your body—and as a consequence, you will notice and feel nothing.

You could be in the most beautiful place, and you'll say something like, "Oh, that's pretty," but then you're on to the next thing. That's disconnection. Everyone has felt it at one time or another, and many of us feel it constantly.

Connection, on the other hand, is also something that everyone has experienced. In a connected state, you feel open, more alive, and able to experience what is right in front of you. You may feel a sense of collaboration, whether it is with a human or more-than-human; you are part of a shared moment. Connection feels good. Because it feels so good, we sometimes seek to fabricate moments of feeling connected in ultimately unsustainable ways—through casual sex, adventure-based sports, or even drugs or alcohol. But you may have noticed the downside—it doesn't last and leaves you wanting more. Whether we realize it or not, we have been searching for connection since the day we were born. Connection with the world around us, but also feeling connected to ourselves.

I have great compassion for my younger self, that version of me who felt so lost on the mountain. I want to note that as you embark on this work of reuniting your body and your mind, please do so with compassion for yourself. If I could have a conversation with that younger me, I would tell her the same thing I say to you now: There is nothing wrong with you. You're doing the best you can. You may not be feeling at home in your body, but you are not alone. In fact, it has become so normal that disconnection is our new standard. On your way back to connection, compassion may be found through understanding—understanding how we, as humans, got to this point of disconnection. Let's shine a light on the various ways disconnection shows up in life in order to bring awareness, as awareness creates an opportunity for change.

## Constriction: A Biological Response Gone Awry

There is an intense feeling of constriction in the modern world. Have you noticed it? Can you feel it right now? What is that feeling and where does it come from?

Constriction can be a physiological response to a perceived threat—feeling the need to disconnect or close off in order to protect. If you've ever seen a young child yelled at by an adult, you might have observed their little body physically close in on themselves. We are all like that, but it might not be visible to others around us. As adults the stressor might be the news, a challenging boss or partner, or the fact that there is so much happening that we feel bombarded. We constrict to keep ourselves safe. We begin to close off because it is all too much. We round our shoulders, close our hearts, or perhaps look away. And in this bubble of self-protection, all of a sudden, we don't see other people and even lose touch with ourselves.

The constriction response is biological, primal, and it's logical. When a forager eats a plant, and it makes their belly hurt, they will not eat that plant again. Our bodies learn "good from bad." Our bodies have developed this response in order to keep us safe.

Language reveals our innate knowledge of the connections between the emotional and the physical body. People will describe something someone said to them as, "A hit, a blow, a gut punch." We can be listening to the news and receive a gut punch—one that might almost make us coil over. Most of us are receiving gut punches every single day. Off-the-charts stress in our culture has made the feeling of constriction a normal part of our lives.

This cycle of constriction and recoil, which leads to disconnection, has its roots in the brain. Threatening sensory information received can sound the alarm, firing up our brain's amygdala, which is a much faster responder than the higher-level processing of the prefrontal cortex. What happens next is an automatic response: the body takes action before it assesses the situation for an actual emergency. Both the nervous system and endocrine system (which produces stress hormones) spring into action—the body responds as if there is a true life-threatening emergency—ready to fight or get the heck out of there.

The child who is regularly yelled at is stuck. Their system is revved up with no options except to constrict or disconnect. This cycle is repeated in different situations but with similar results—this patterned response of recoiling or disconnecting gets "hardwired" in. At some point in our lives, we have all been that child—different experience, but similar outcome. As you unfurl from constriction, remember to have great tenderness and compassion for yourself.

## Lifestyle Disconnection

Stress is the health epidemic of the twenty-first century and is at unsustainable levels for both our bodies and the natural world. If your inner landscape is occupied with chronic stress, it will always seem like something is missing in your life. Chronic stress takes over the body like an invasive plant, causing the inner flowers to wither.

We try to disconnect from stress by disconnecting from the world around us. But unfortunately, we haven't disconnected from the root of much of our stress, the mind. We focus on thoughts about the past or future, on mistakes made, on things left undone, or on problems yet to be solved. Problem-solving and "figuring out" are how most of us spend the majority of our waking hours. In this stress cycle, we over-effort, believing we can actually control life, which is impossible.

Pay attention when you are in "control mode." Ironically, it leads to disconnection. Notice the side effects in your body: physical tension, emotions coming up that are unrelated to the problem at hand, a sense of being weighed down, or pressure in your head or heart. These are all signs that you are no longer seeing and connecting with what is around you. The stories in your mind have built a wall around you, and you are connecting only with them.

Disconnection begins at a young age in our culture. If you're a dreamer or a creator, those parts of yourself often get stamped out in traditional education, where there is no free time for it to develop. Creativity and exploration take time and spaciousness. So, to work within the constraints of a system, you have to conform. By the time kids graduate high school, they have learned to distrust their own uniqueness. They become adults who are spinning because they have lost their own bearings. They have no idea where their north is. They then become adults who feel like they are always putting out fires. They disconnect and numb out with alcohol, food, sex, or endless hours of working or scrolling the internet.

Most Americans are proud of the hard-working ethos that many of our grandparents exemplified. We are proud of ourselves if we work hard and even prouder if we work harder! But the fact is, it's an illusion to think that an eighty-hour work week makes anything better. In fact, it's been proven that in the long run, working too much is actually ineffective. Creativity begins to dwindle, and people miss out on the big picture. Tunnel focus sets in, a narrow mindset becomes narrower, and disconnection becomes more pronounced.

Add to these stresses lifestyles that induce loneliness. We can go days without interacting in the same space with another person or spending time outdoors. Our groceries are left at our door, much of our work can be done on a computer, and we can see others through social media and video platforms. But living so independently is detrimental to our well-being. Through Zoom, social media, and text we get a little hit of connection with each other, but it is not a full-bodied experience. Researchers have found that a lack of healthy connections with others leads to depression and can be detrimental to physical health. Unlike in the natural world, where everything is interconnected, our primal need for connection goes unmet.

We have "adapted" to extremely high levels of stress and sensory overload. We are revving our engines really high all day, every day; and we are just not meant to run that way for more than brief periods. For most people, the only signal to stop is when the body begins to break down. But even then, early-stress symptoms are so normal in our culture that they are often just medicated or ignored. Below is a list of stress-related symptoms, according to the Mayo Clinic.[1] Are any of them familiar to you?

- Headache
- Muscle tension or pain
- Restlessness
- Lack of motivation or focus
- Fatigue
- Feeling overwhelmed
- Irritability or anger
- Social withdrawal
- Stomach upset
- Sadness or depression
- Overeating or undereating
- Sleep problems

We tolerate these symptoms, but they are shots across the bow—warning signs of a system out of balance. But just because it's possible to ignore these subtle symptoms doesn't mean that you should. If they aren't acknowledged by lifestyle adjustment, our bodies will continue to try and get our attention through steadily worsening symptoms of stress:

high blood pressure, heart disease, obesity, diabetes, and other health problems, both physical and mental.

## Anxiety

One of my greatest teachers was the ten-year relationship I had with anxiety. Though my symptoms started off mild, anxiety eventually eroded away my sense of freedom. Sometimes I got full-body hives. Sometimes I felt like I was spinning. There were even times when I couldn't drive at night on highways because it would trigger a panic attack. Anxiety controlled my life.

Anxiety controls a lot of people's lives. In fact, I've met very few people who have no experience with it. Start asking yourself a few questions and you may begin to notice that anxiety is controlling you or causing you to disconnect in subtle ways. Next time you choose not to go somewhere or do something, ask yourself: Why am I choosing not to do that? What's the why behind the no? Is it anxiety? As a dear therapist friend of mine says, "Is this a fear-based response or a wise mind response?"

My own struggles have given me great compassion for the countless individuals who battle with anxiety daily. But I want to note that although anxiety is extremely normal in our culture, anxiety is not a natural state—period. If you are experiencing anxiety, this is an indicator light signaling that your system needs a reset. Anxiety is like a friend saying, "Hey! How you're navigating the world is not working for you." If you experience anxiety, feel grateful for it. It is giving you the wakeup call that you need.

## Empaths

An empathic person feels a lot of what other people are feeling. You probably know an empathic person, or perhaps you are one yourself. As a child I could feel people's stress so acutely that I learned to almost step out of my body; other people's emotions were too much for me. I didn't know how to deal with them. The world felt overwhelming.

Some empathic people's boundaries can be unclear; it can be hard for them to know where they end, and others begin. Empaths feel the world, and they're often hurting. So, it is easy to see why they are particularly prone to disconnection. For an empath, it becomes even more important to find ways to safely connect with the body rather than disconnect. Taking up space within the body creates a natural boundary. Imagine the light of your consciousness or presence completely filling your body. As you inhabit your body, you become less penetrable to other people's "stuff," in a good and healthy way.

However, the superpower of the empath is to be able to put themselves in another person's shoes. This makes for amazingly kind, caring, and compassionate people. A lot of therapists, and a lot of people in service fields tend to be empaths. In order to survive, you don't have to turn off your empathetic self—we need you. Nature will prove to be one of your biggest allies.

## Trauma

Trauma can cause disconnection at its most intense—resulting in disconnecting from ourselves and the world around us. Many of us have experienced traumatic events or situations that caused so much pain and suffering that we may have disconnected from the part within us that was experiencing the suffering. With trauma, even after the danger is over, the disconnection remains.

Trauma can manifest itself in many forms. If you have experienced heartbreak, the pain might have been so much that you unconsciously closed off your heart in order to not feel such intense pain again. At the time of the traumatic event(s), that response was helpful, but now it limits your capacity to receive and give love. If you have experienced physical or emotional abuse, your body has learned to feel unsafe. You might have unconsciously disconnected from your body, or parts of your body, as a protective mechanism. If you were told repeatedly as a child that you were too much or not enough, that may have caused you to disconnect from your personal power.

There is inherent brilliance in your response to the trauma you experienced. You were resilient and adapted to life so you could continue forward during a really difficult time. But unfortunately, it can be challenging to unlearn the response to the trauma once it is gone. Sometimes, responses and adaptations to trauma from the past are so deeply embedded that their influence on daily life is hard to detect. However, with the light of awareness in the here and now, you can begin to be curious about how the past is impacting your present. Is the trauma response serving you anymore, or is it getting in your way?

Trauma is not your fault. It is stored in the body, and it is here that we must return to unfurl the trauma response.[2,3] If you have experienced trauma that is impacting your life, the processes in this book can help you, but move through them slowly and with great compassion for yourself. Nature will meet you where you are and match your pace. Trauma can be deep-seated and takes time to heal. A trusted therapist that understands the mind-body connection can be very beneficial as well.

The good news is the parts of ourselves that feel lost due to trauma are not gone. They are still with us, waiting to be welcomed home. Like a frightened child hiding behind a parent, they will emerge and begin to explore when conditions appear to be safe. Slowly, and eventually, they will begin to play, create, and engage with others.

## The Normalization of Disconnection

A lot of people who sign up for my retreats come because they are trying to reclaim parts of themselves that have been forgotten. Something is missing in their lives, but they can't quite pinpoint what. For many, this missing piece is actually where they are not looking—or rather, where they are not feeling. It's the body where the richness of life is felt. But most people can't distinguish this as a problem because almost everyone experiences this. So, how can disconnectedness even be recognized for what it is? Like anything, if we turn our attention to the clues with fresh eyes, we can see what was once hidden.

On the page that follows is a table with subtle clues—feelings associated with not being at home in your body, not embodied, and clues that you are embodied. See if any of these sound familiar.

Like anxiety symptoms, these symptoms of being outside of your body are a shot across the bow. They are your warning. Mild symptoms can easily be ignored, but don't ignore them. As they become more acute, they may manifest as depression, anxiety, and loneliness.

There is an antidote. For all those moments that caused you to constrict, you need that many more moments to soften, to open, to feel safe. As adults, those parts of us that disconnected or went into hiding can emerge if we create safe conditions, and that is what Nature can so powerfully provide. In Nature, you will feel the walls around your heart being gently deconstructed, your personal power reclaimed, and your body, mind, and soul becoming safe again.

| NOT EMBODIED<br>living in your mind | EMBODIED<br>living in your body |
|---|---|
| A feeling of unsettledness or uncertainty | A feeling of calm |
| Indecisiveness | Able to make clear decisions |
| Shallow breath, up high in your chest | Breath finds its way towards the belly |
| Feeling foggy headed | Clarity in thought |
| Most of your feelings and sensations occur up in your head or you experience head pressure | Feeling yourself standing or sitting |
| Numbness: You want to feel joy and excitement, but you can't access those states in your body | You are moved by what is happening in the moment<br><br>You can feel it in your body |
| A feeling of swirling on the inside | A feeling of being steady |
| You feel like something's missing, but you can't put your finger on it | You feel at peace |
| You tend to bump into things | You have spatial awareness of what is around you |

## Nature Deficit Disorder

In 2005, Richard Louv coined the phrase "nature-deficit disorder" to serve as a description of the human costs of alienation from Nature, especially with regards to children.[4] I believe an engaged relationship with Nature is the missing piece for human health and well-being.

This chapter has shined a light on disconnection. At some point, we have all constricted, or closed off our hearts, to some things, or many things. It can seem safer to think than to feel, and so we become walking heads. But one of the things a walking head is not going to prioritize is spending time in Nature. Why would you? Nature doesn't add to your 401(k)! Nature doesn't check items off your to-do list! But the thesis of this book is that spending time with Nature can heal you. The following chapters will show you how. Through supporting a balanced and vibrant you, Nature can, in fact, add to your bottom line.

If my mental, emotional, or spiritual well-being begins to deteriorate, one of the first questions I ask myself is if I've had enough time in Nature. I find that by attending to that one need, my sense of well-being is restored, every time. Take a moment to do an honest assessment of how you are currently serving this fundamental need. If you find yourself in "the deficit," know you are in the right place to remedy that.

CHAPTER 3

# nature's basic teachings

There is a point in every fairy tale when the hero or heroine on a journey can't go any further. All seems lost, including their physical and mental strength. It is often in these lowest moments in the story that a miracle will occur—an ally or guide will appear. That guide points the way to inner resource and strength in the hero or heroine, allowing them to return home.

Retreating to Nature for wisdom and awakening is woven into the tapestry of every culture. Siddhartha Gautama sat under the Bodhi tree and achieved enlightenment, becoming the Buddha. Hebrew prophets spoke from the wilderness. After his baptism, Jesus went into the wilderness for forty days, where he spoke truth to what was evil, and became a full expression of himself. Countless mystics, sages, and shamans have called to our souls to return to the wild truth and freedom that can be found in Nature.

I have experienced months at a time backpacking in the woods, and I can attest those were extremely transformative for me. With the world's distractions gone, I became still enough that I could hear Nature whispering in my ear. I also wrestled with my shadows, because within the stillness of Nature, the shadows of the mind had nowhere to hide.

However, as important as those experiences were to me, I will be the first to tell you that it is not necessary for you to go live in the wilderness for months in order to experience transformation. In fact, you don't even have to go very far from your house or your office. In this chapter, we'll begin learning some of the fundamental lessons that Nature teaches, and you can experience every one of these truths from just outside your door.

I believe the following lessons are essential for the journey of coming home to your body and living a passionate and authentic life of connection. I'm excited to share them with you.

## NATURE'S LESSON 1:
## Nourishment, Community, and Rest

Nature offered me a hands-on lesson in healing when I was a Forestry graduate student at the University of Georgia. My research site, along a country road outside of Sandersville, in South Georgia, had a particularly challenging history. The land had been stripped of its timber to grow cotton in the 1800s. Cotton farming robbed the land of its topsoil, and after the fields were depleted, the land was mined for its mineral, kaolin. By the time I arrived on it, that patch of land was as used-up as any land could get.

That patch of land, with its mix of red clay subsoil and remaining white kaolin, was my responsibility for the course of my graduate studies. It was absolutely devoid of life. My research to reclaim it for the benefit of wildlife and tree production was a daunting task, to say the least.

So, I began at the beginning. It was obvious that the land was in serious need of nourishment. My colleagues and I applied compost, and then seeded the ground with nitrogen-fixing plants. The roots of these plants are colonized by bacteria that extract nitrogen from the air making it available in a form usable for plant growth. Next, we cultivated a community of diverse plants that benefited wildlife by creating a food source and habitat. Finally, we did something that seems counterintuitive in our modern culture: we stopped working to give the land time to rest. It was during this rest time that the drastically disturbed soil began to heal. Through the growing microbial and invertebrate populations such as earthworms, woodlice, snails, and millipedes; the plant communities of native grasses and pine trees; and the wildlife returning—the land began to reclaim herself, but we had to get out of the way.

If given just the tiniest levels of support, Nature will predictably heal herself. After all, this has been going on for thousands of years! However, to see a barren wasteland transform into a productive ecosystem within a relatively short time absolutely amazed me. Within two years, the mottled red and white clay landscape, which looked like a different planet, became a sea of green. The land simply took the nourishment, community, and rest that we offered, and used those ingredients to recover—completely. Since then, I've witnessed this same phenomenon elsewhere, including in brownfield lots in New York City—barren, often polluted urban areas, devoid of life, have transformed right before my eyes.

If any system's natural adaptive response is overwhelmed, it will begin to break down. Many of us have experienced ill health, neglect, or abuse, just like that patch of land. But if you ever think it's too late to make profound changes, please remember that patch of land in South Georgia. Through nourishment, connecting with community, and rest, we can reclaim our health and well-being on all levels, just like that land did.

## NATURE'S LESSON 2:
## Flow

Imagine clinging to a rock in the middle of a fast-moving river. You're trying to hang on, but it takes a tremendous amount of effort not to go with the flow of water. Trying to control situations in our life requires the same amount of effort. It is exhausting.

Now imagine you let go of the rock, lie back, and allow yourself to flow in the current with ease. All of a sudden, without effort, you are moving in the direction you want to be heading. Nature is the ultimate guide to going with the flow because water is always taking the path of least resistance. Obstructions? What obstructions? It just flows around them.

Have you ever felt in the flow—or, as some say, in the zone? Most likely, you felt a heightened sense of aliveness or excitement about life or the project you were working on. The right ideas came forth effortlessly. Support, or the right person, came to you from what seemed out of nowhere. In this state, you were allowing yourself to flow like water.

Flow states can lead to feelings of exhilaration, bliss, timelessness, and effortlessness. When in the flow, individuals are fully immersed in their experience, and also aware of their internal state. Mihaly Csikszentmihalyi, psychologist and professor who coined the term flow, defines it as "A state in which people are so involved in an activity that nothing else seems to matter. The experience is so enjoyable that people will continue to do it even at great cost, for the sheer sake of doing it."[1]

Many of us have experienced states of flow when on vacation, or on a retreat. These are moments when we have stepped away from our regular routine and feel more open to possibilities. The novelty of our new surroundings and new sensory input helps keep us in the present moment.

However, after the experience is over, we sometimes become deflated as we enter back into our regular routine.

Is it possible to bring flow to your everyday life? I believe it is. You can cultivate flow through present moment awareness, becoming grounded in your body, opening your heart, and feeling gratitude. When we approach the natural world with these states, Nature can guide us into a flow state, right where we are. The practices in this book are designed to be the bridge to connect you with Nature's flow.

## NATURE'S LESSON 3:
### Embracing Cycles of Life and Death

Just as life bursts forth in the spring to produce fruit, offspring, and growth, Nature also gracefully demonstrates what it means to die. Flowers go to seed. Leaves fall from trees. A mountain slowly weathers to the ground. But with each letting go, new life emerges: in a seed, fallen leaves support the next growing season through nutrients released as they decompose, and new soil forms from the mountain as its rock is weathered by the wind, rain, and freezing/thawing.

As you sit with Nature and witness her cycles, you will begin to witness the cycles within your life. You will eventually develop the ability to feel these cycles without the need to control them. For example, you might begin to see wrinkles on your face—beautiful and noble as the rings on a tree—as a symbol of the passage of time. You will learn to honor the need for rest, as you witness how your body feels at different times. You can even witness the cycles of friendships, which might grow and shift.

When you learn to flow with all of your cycles, you suffer less. Death is part of the cycle and, understandably can evoke deep emotions.

Navigating life through being with what is and honoring the cycle you are in, helps alleviate fear and the desire to control life.

## NATURE'S LESSON 4:
### Embodiment—Coming Home to Your Body

Being embodied is being physically, emotionally, and spiritually in your body. This may sound like something that you are already doing. But as we discovered in chapter two, many of us have learned to exist more in our minds than in our physical selves.

Coming home to your body, or embodiment, is at the core of this book, and this principle is beautifully and regularly displayed in Nature. Animals utilize their minds but are not dominated by their minds. That's because the present moment is where all of Nature dwells. A squirrel caches away nuts for the winter but is fully in the present moment as it is doing so. Forgotten acorns become the gift of trees for future generations with minimal effort. The squirrel was just doing the next right thing in the present moment.

Peter Levine—psychotherapist, author of the best-selling book *Waking the Tiger: Healing Trauma*, and founder of the Somatic Experiencing® model, applies the wisdom of the animal world to healing trauma in the human body. Through his work, Levine has brought to light the freeze response to trauma when fight or flight isn't an option. The freeze response is an altered state of feeling no pain or dissociating from the body when pain is too much to endure. Under attack from a predator, even though frozen, an animal's internal world is abuzz with intense energy searching for an escape. Once free, there is an instinctual release of internal energy through movement—often through running or shaking. Their nervous system resets itself, and the animal can return to an embodied state. They can fully be in their body again and proceed back to life as usual.

When humans enter the freeze response state, sometimes the "thawing out" stage doesn't happen. The movement or action needed to discharge the tremendous amount of internal energy doesn't occur, and this keeps us from transitioning back to our bodies in their pre-traumatized state. Peter Levine states "Humans suffer when we are unable to discharge the energy that is locked in by the freeze response."[2] We get stuck in a disembodied or frozen state.

When you are truly embodied, you feel alive and energized. There is increased energy running through your body because you're there. You can feel it. When you are disembodied, you operate mainly within your brain. The result is brain fog, head pressure, and mental fatigue. There is little space for your creativity and brilliance.

As we drop down into the body, we create more space in our minds. In a state of embodiment, we have more access to wonder and excitement. All the energy we have invested in controlling situations becomes available for creative efforts instead. Life becomes an exploration rather than something to "get through" or "manage."

Feelings of embodiment and flow are what people are seeking in activities like adventure sports. They want to feel in their bodies—to feel fully awake. When you become intentionally embodied, you can feel that way every day. You don't have to jump out of a plane! Your senses will become sharper. You'll see things you didn't see, hear things you didn't hear, and perceive the world like never before—all your senses become fully functional. When you are embodied, you feel and sense your body. You will take up your space within it and, like our animal brethren, you will perceive real threats versus ones that exist only in your mind.

## NATURE'S LESSON 5:
### Getting Grounded

Unlike the winged ones in the air, or finned ones in the ocean, we have feet—and they are designed to tread softly on the earth. Form *follows* function is an iconic phrase in biology that basically means the form of the body part "tells" you what that part does, what its function is. Our feet are designed not only to get us around—they connect and ground us to the earth, as well. When you allow your feet to serve their full function, you navigate this stress-filled world with more ease and grace.

Years ago, I studied energy medicine in Asheville, NC, and my teacher often told me, "Kathleen, you need to get grounded. Get IN your feet! Get IN your body!" At that point, those words meant nothing to me. I had no idea how to get IN my body. I didn't even understand what she meant.

However, through years of experimentation and practice with Nature, eventually I learned that being grounded is a felt awareness of the body and a state of being. Since one of the functions of our feet is to connect us with the earth, it is through our feet that we can quickly return to a state of groundedness. Try this with me right now. Draw your attention to your feet by first wiggling your toes. Now feel the subtle sensations within your feet. Can you feel their connection with the earth? Taking your shoes off and standing on the earth is helpful for this. Now, take a deep breath, and as you exhale, allow your breath and energy to rest, or drop into your feet. This takes practice at first, because most of the time, our awareness is at its farthest point from our feet—in our mind. However, groundedness is our most natural way of being in the world, as we are people of the land, people of the earth.

Groundedness is also a state of being—I am here, I am settled into the clay of my body, and I feel solid.

Being grounded supports your nervous system. A good metaphor for this is a grounding wire used in electrical systems. During a power surge, extra electricity can travel safely back to the earth rather than frying the system. Grounding works this way for humans, as well. If you are grounded, stress around you is less likely to fry your operating system. The extra energy can move safely through or around you, back down to the earth. Grounded people can find themselves surrounded by various types of energy and be just fine. They are the calm in the center of any storm.

## NATURE'S LESSON 6:
## Oneness

I have written the majority of this field guide next to the beautiful pecan tree in my backyard. I decided to ask this tree for clarity on how to articulate the state of Oneness with all life. It can be challenging to feel this, nonetheless put into words. The immediate response I received was that Oneness IS.

Nature demonstrates Oneness beautifully.

If we listen and feel the "ISness" of water, "ISness" of a tree, or "ISness" of fire, eventually we learn to claim "ISness" for ourselves. To experience the "ISness" of another, we drop all preconceived notions and settle into their presence with our full embodied awareness and our spiritual sight (beyond what we can see with our eyes). "ISness" is a state free of labels—you, water, the earth—free to be a full expression of itself, limitless, an integrated whole, sweetly connected with all of life.

Ilia Delio, theologian and scientist, writes: "Human life must be traced back to the time when life was deeply one, a Singularity, whereby the intensity of mass-energy exploded into consciousness."[3] This Singularity is the origin of our Oneness with all of life.

Humans consciously and unconsciously separate themselves from feeling unified with Nature.

Oneness is interconnection, the common threads that weave together all of creation. But why should a tree or water get to experience the interconnectedness of all life, and you don't? It is only our minds that separate the tree from the water, and the water from all the microbes within.

In Nature (and with practice), you can begin to feel yourself as a unique being and simultaneously part of the whole divine tapestry of creation, a part of all that is. Nature will show you that it's safe to trust and even that it's safe to let go.

You will feel vital and important because you will know your place in the Oneness. Again, this is a very difficult concept to articulate, and that is why the majority of this book is dedicated to exercises that you can try rather than read about! You will recognize Oneness when you feel it.

## NATURE'S LESSON 7:
### Awakening the Heart

Although the brain is the primary human navigational system, it may surprise you to learn that you have another one. The heart is a navigational device, and it guides us quite differently than the brain.

As we have learned already, journeying with the mind alone keeps us wandering in circles, believing tales concocted from past experiences—tales that are often tainted by fear. But there is another way to experience life. Bringing your awakened heart back online and fully operational is like shining a light in the darkness. As Antoine de Saint-Exupéry so beautifully articulated in The Little Prince, "It is only with the heart that one can see rightly; what is essential is invisible to the eye."[4]

Nature's lessons about opening the heart are best illustrated in the way we experience her. Oftentimes we see the natural world as if at dusk. The outlines of trees and plants are visible and familiar, but the details are murky and go unnoticed. However, when we are experiencing Nature with the awareness of our hearts, consciously connecting, she feels—and looks—quite different. Instead of thinking, "Oh, there is a rock, there is a tree, there is a flower," you are experiencing their beauty and depth. You feel an inner movement and sense of connection. The process of awakening the heart means slowing down, coaxing your body and your consciousness to allow more heart guidance and less head guidance.

At this point, it may seem hard to imagine how you might get from "normal, everyday" human consciousness to a state of being embodied, grounded, and experiencing life from your heart. But I am here to show you a clear pathway. My own journey was a long and challenging one, but yours will be much smoother! Let's continue by exploring what it means to be nourished.

FIELD NOTES

# nourishment redefined

Nourishment is often used as a synonym for food, which omits several important aspects of this word. This limitation suggests that the physical body is the only part of ourselves that needs nourishing. In fact, all aspects of our being receive and respond to nourishment. Many of the choices that we make emotionally, mentally, physically, and spiritually either nourish or support these aspects of ourselves or undernourish them, potentially causing harm. With the mind-body-spirit connection, each aspect needs to be tended to and nourished, as they are intricately connected, and each influences the other. If you are struggling or undernourished emotionally, there is a good chance this is impacting you physically, mentally, and spiritually, as well.

When struggling with any aspect of ourselves, we naturally look to soothe, find comfort, and fill what seems to be a void. It can be easy to reach for a quick fix—for things that temporarily make us feel better or distract us—such as food, alcohol, overworking, drugs, or social media. Advertisers are ingenious at marketing to our pain points by offering "solutions" which often leave us feeling empty or even worse than before. We have access to so much but, at the same time, are so undernourished.

In order to grow, be well, and thrive, we need to be nourished at all levels. Nourishment is an important foundation to creating change and embarking on this journey. But what does healthy, long-lasting nourishment mean? What does it look and feel like?

Let's uncover its deeper meaning by beginning with honest, compassionate observation. Ask yourself: Am I struggling in my body? Am I struggling in my mind? Am I emotionally all over the place? Has it been a long time since I felt excited and passionate about something? A nourished system doesn't suffer as intensely as an undernourished one, so if your answer to any of the above questions was "yes," then let's look deeply at how you are nourishing yourself. That is a good place to start finding answers.

## Earth My Body

I love the idea of our bodies being of the earth. Your earthen form—its softness, its rounded parts, its sensuous parts—is a vessel to be delighted in, as are all elements of Nature. Your body is not something to escape or transcend, but to settle into, like the most exquisite piece of pottery.

We often don't see our bodies as works of art. Why do we try to drastically change this beautiful form that we are born into? Why do we deprive it? Why do we try to make our body something that fits into a mold that was never meant to be? The answers are multilayered and woven into much of the fabric of our societies. Some religious thought reinforces disconnection from the body through shame of its sensuous nature. Some of us have been taught to deny or to transcend our physical form. And almost every single one of us has been given false, distorted images by social media and advertising of what the body should look like and even what the body is for. Compounding all of this is the unconscious disconnect from the inherent goodness of our earthen form as a result of traumatic experiences. I believe there is a different way. As you rediscover and settle into the *earth of your body*, you will feel its strength and revel in its form.

The body is temporary; though we try to defy the aging process, it happens. What if we were as fascinated by the wrinkles on someone's face as the rings on a tree? Nature offers us a guide on how to inhabit the *earth of our body*: each element of Nature, although temporary, accepts itself entirely for what it is. A tree is not trying to be anything other than a tree. It sprouts, grows towards the sky, produces nuts, and one day falls. When did we stop accepting ourselves for who we are? When I am in the woods for an extended period, away from mirrors and common culture, I find that I can let my body serve the function of being my vessel, just as it is. I affirm and celebrate myself, content being me.

From that vantage point, it's hard to understand how I could be harsh towards myself, undervalue my earthen form, and make choices that aren't nourishing. However, none of us live entirely in the wild. Most of the time, we live in society, which is a much more complicated place to be. As we can all attest, the choices we make in society are usually biased and multilayered.

## Food

Plants thrive in nutrient-rich soil with appropriate access to water and sunlight. In these conditions, they grow stronger, produce a greater yield, and are more resistant to disease, insect infestation, and drought. This very simple lesson can be applied to human health and wellness: Eating nutrient-rich food in its most natural form helps the mind and the body to feel clear and adapt to environmental stressors.

That seems simple enough, but it's strangely easier said than done. However, if you consider the busyness of our daily lives, perhaps not so strange after all. For most of us, the tightrope that we walk between doing right by our bodies and relieving our stress through food (or other substances) is a precarious one.

Our inner landscape offers ample information about our nutritional choices. Exhaustion, brain fog, or indigestion are symptoms relatively easy to pinpoint if you allow yourself to look for them. Yet, it's easier for us to ignore our own warning signals than it is the wilting potted plant on the shelf in need of water and light. Why is it less complicated to get nourishment for a plant than to achieve optimum nourishment for a human?

Maybe it's because humans are "complex (in a beautiful way)!" As stated above, we are a lot more than just physical.

We have many aspects that need nourishing in order to live well, and it is in finding this balance (or not finding it) that many of our choices about food are made. An overworked nervous system, an exhausted mind, an emotional system in upheaval, or an undernourished spirit may cause you to make food choices that aren't so nourishing or supportive.

Tending to the emotional, mental, or spiritual parts of yourself has the potential to positively impact how you physically nourish yourself. If your relationship with food is not supportive or perhaps even harmful, be gentle with yourself. Through the practices in this book, you will nourish all parts of you, and over time, your relationship with food will likely shift.

In the spirit of learning through experience, I've got something for you to try that may help to simplify the complexity around eating and provide you with the minerals and nutrients you need to thrive. Take a weekly trip to the Farmer's market. Local produce is reflective of the types of foods that are most nourishing each season, and because they are fresher, they have a higher nutrient content—and the bonus of a lower carbon footprint. Your food choices should make you feel good, not in a temporary way, but satiated for the long-term.

In our quest to feel in control of our lives, some people regulate their food intake to the point of stress. I'm referring to undernourishment, excessive dieting, and on-again, off-again dieting. If we equated eating to energy production, like in the natural world, the word dieting would be nonexistent. Animals in the wild eat what they need to survive and to produce offspring. They have an awareness of their bodies and can give them what they need as long as resources are available. We have lost our body awareness in exchange for counting calories or following the most popular diet. Be kind to yourself, be kind to your body, and listen to your body as it will tell you what it needs. Keep listening.

The stress-based nutritional cycle that many of us are caught in—disembodied living giving rise to poor food choices, poor food choices reinforcing disembodied living—can, and will, also work in reverse. A well-nourished system will inspire you to be more in your body, and a properly balanced mind and body can make complicated food choices seem intuitive and easy. Nourishing yourself with kindness and compassion can change normal choices into decisions that are genuinely healing. That is the work of this book.

## Water and Air

As with all organisms, our health and well-being depend upon clean water and clean air. But these two needs are harder for us to ensure since they are impacted and shared by so many. You may feel disempowerment around the subject of pollution—even contemplating it may take you instantly to a place of stress. Bringing stress into your body is the opposite of my intention for this book! With that said, I have a few simple suggestions I would like to share.

The first is to drink high-quality water. If you have well water, get your water tested for a range of organic and inorganic substances. And for those of us on city water, there are many great water filters on the market that can remove the majority of water contaminants remaining after municipality filtration. Invest in the highest quality one you can afford.

Regulating the quality of air that is going into your body is a lot trickier than water. It's an area where you may feel helpless, at best. But there is actually something you can do to help improve the air quality in your neighborhood and world: You can become an advocate for trees, prairie restoration, or mangrove protection. That may sound like something from a children's story, but it is quite real and very impactful.

Trees and plants are our first set of lungs. They are natural air filters. They, along with the ocean phytoplankton, are our source of life-giving oxygen. The more trees planted, and land protected, the better off we all are. So, if you are negatively impacted by air pollution in your area, or are concerned about global warming, turn your fear into positive action by becoming a champion for good air quality. You can do this by planting trees and conserving land or supporting those who do. Find your local lands conservancy organization and join it. You will be more informed and forge deeper connections with your natural neighborhood. This tiny step can help you heal the air you breathe, and it will lessen the disempowerment you may feel around air quality. Both will have tangible effects.

## Rest

Every winter, we witness Nature taking a rest. Farmers using best agricultural practices rotate their crops in order to give fields time to rest and replenish. Within faith traditions, there is a sabbath, a day of rest. But despite these beautiful examples, most of us keep pushing forward, seven days a week, three hundred sixty-five days a year, as if we humans are somehow separated from the laws that govern Nature. And as with nutrition, although a lack of rest has simple and straightforward solutions, they are often strangely hard to put into practice.

According to the Division of Sleep Medicine at Harvard Medical School, sleep is so important that even slight sleep deprivation or poor-quality sleep can affect memory, judgment, and mood.[1] The amount of sleep you need might change depending on the season or what is going on in your life, but chances are good that you need more than you're currently getting. Ask yourself honestly: Am I getting enough quality rest?

One recommendation I share with my clients who have a hard time sleeping is to treat themselves like they would a baby, literally. Think about it: Would you keep your baby up late at night on a screen and then expect that baby to sleep? No way! You would give your baby a nice warm bath. You would dim the lights, perhaps play soft music, dress them in cozy clothes, and gently put them to bed. And then, you would encourage your baby to sleep for *as long as their body wants*.

This method is very simple, and it's how we would naturally treat ourselves. However, these behaviors are very hard for most of us to actually adopt. Learning how to do genuine self-care—or giving yourself permission to treat yourself very gently and well—is part of the work of this book. These are real skills. Treating yourself well is a practice.

Rest also means more than just sleeping. Like many of you, I start my day at 5:00 am, and I keep going until bedtime. However, I am intentional about creating microdoses of rest with Nature in all her forms (practices in section two are my go-tos). In these brief moments, my nervous system has a chance to restore and reset. Longer periods of rest are also very nourishing and necessary. For example, can you create a day, or half a day, once a week in which you are intentionally unproductive? Literally, schedule time on your calendar to do nothing productive. Going further, unplug. It's surprisingly difficult to unplug from devices for an entire day. Try it, though, and I promise that you will find your other six days of the week more focused, more inspired, and more productive.

Nature gifts us the lesson of rest. Our bodies experience a biochemical response when we pause and connect with Nature, and that response is restoration. When I'm outdoors in Nature, I can feel myself settling into my body. My forehead and shoulders soften, and thoughts float past without getting stuck in mental processing. That is real rest.

In the next few chapters, you will begin to learn how to do it. It's my promise that when practiced regularly, connecting with Nature—inside and out—will change your life immensely.

## Energy Discharge

Anxiety can be a byproduct of overstimulation. Babies who are overstimulated will "cry it out" to discharge their excess energy. But sometimes, we are just as overstimulated as those babies and don't allow ourselves to release healthfully. At times it's like we have put our finger into an electric socket, hyper-charging our nervous system, and now it's frazzled. So, we need to find healthy ways to discharge that buzzing.

The practices in this book are my recommendations for gently pressing the release valve daily, as many can be done almost anywhere, at any time. But sometimes, when a situation is acute, it helps to call in the reserves: massage, good chiropractic care, acupuncture, an Epsom salt bath, or even going to a salt room can help you process that buzzing before it becomes something more toxic in your body. I highly recommend bodywork from a safe, grounded, and trusted individual, particularly for people who suffer from anxiety.

A critical first step in energy discharge is recognizing when you need it. One clue is when you can't settle down; you can almost feel yourself buzzing, on the verge of getting triggered by something minor, or your thoughts are whirling dervishes. You feel uncomfortable or irritable, and you hear yourself saying something like, "I could really use a massage," or "I really need a bath"—that might be just the medicine you need for discharge. When you respond to an inner request or act on your intuition about what your body needs, you start building a safety network within yourself. Parts of you that were not well taken care of in the past begin to feel nurtured and safe; this is healing. Tending to the body begins with recognizing when the body needs tending.

## Movement

Have you noticed how you feel more energized when your body is flexible and moving rather than stagnant? A flexible and moving body supports the flow of lymphatic fluid, blood, oxygen, and energy with ease. If body parts become stagnant, our health and well-being can experience disharmony.

Reflecting back on how animals "unfreeze" themselves after a traumatic incident provides a clear lesson for humans. What do the other animals do? They move, often with a great burst of energy. Movement not only nourishes our body but can also unlock trauma and release stored emotions. There is great wisdom in the classic Qigong movement of shaking the body. This practice is exactly what it sounds like—standing in a stable yet flexible position and gently bouncing and shaking each part of your body. Not only does this release you from stagnation, but it also reenacts what many animals intuitively do to release and discharge energy. Without the release or movement of energy, individuals can remain frozen in a trauma response which results in hyperarousal and disconnection from the body.

Many clients that I work with know about the benefits of meditation. However, there is also a common misconception that stillness is a requirement of meditation. Traditional stillness practices can sometimes lead to frustration and increase feelings of anxiousness. I have found that for some, sitting still for long periods perpetuates stagnation already within the body. Traditional nonmoving meditation, a very linear, very masculine practice, works wonderfully for some people but not for all people. Women, in particular, often seem to benefit from the invitation to move.

In the last few years, our culture has awakened to the fact that sitting all the time is simply unhealthy. If you're sitting in an office, your mind might be moving constantly, but your body is not. Regular movement is one of your real needs—your birthright as an animal! The kind of movement you choose is up to you, and it can be an easy and intuitive choice. Do what you like. But if you don't have some kind of regular exercise or movement practice in your life, start one as soon as possible. Begin simply—a morning or evening walk can be done anywhere and adjusted to any schedule.

## Community

A yucca plant is entirely dependent on the yucca moth to pollinate it. In return, the yucca moth's larvae depend on some of the plant's seeds for sustenance. One organism cannot exist without the other, and the yucca plant/moth is just one of many examples of how the web of life is not a metaphor— it is quite literal. Nature functions within a dynamic web of connections, from the microbes in the soil to the eagles flying overhead. I encourage you to remember your place within this web every day! Even if you spend all your time in an office building, looking at a computer, you are still a part of Nature. Nature is your community. People are also your community. We need others to be truly well.

One of the many beautiful lessons that Nature demonstrates related to community is the importance of diversity. The more diverse an ecosystem, often the healthier it is. The same applies to the communities we find ourselves in, both human and more-than-human. Our life experience becomes much richer when it includes people with different ideas, backgrounds, beliefs, and dreams than our own. Think about New York City; the diversity of people makes it one of the most creative, vibrant, and inspiring cities in the world. Diversity matters greatly, both in the human and more-than-human world.

And paradoxically, being part of a diverse community can be challenging at times because there are many different perspectives (which is also the beauty of it).

Part of the work of this book is to become so comfortable and at home in your body that you can be with anyone and allow yourself to be fully you and the other person to be fully them. You probably know one or two people who are so comfortable in their own skins that they are happy being around people whose approach to the world is totally different than their own. We need more people like that! And that is precisely the person you will become when you truly inhabit your body. Knowing who you are will allow you to be okay with other people being who they are.

Now that I know how to be in my body, my relational bandwidth has increased. Before, there was an unconscious need to protect myself. As an empath, I had difficulty knowing where I ended, and others began. These days I can say, "I know who I am. I can be with you, and it's great, and you can be just as you are." And if you're doing something that's uncomfortable for me, it's okay—I can choose to stay with you in this space or can choose to leave. Emotional boundaries such as this are an important act of self-love and supportive for living well in community with others. As you do the practices outlined in the following chapters, you'll find that you have more agency of self and likely more acceptance of others.

Good community is a lot like good food. A robust person can process occasional junk food, but a person who is healing needs to be much more careful. As you embark on this practice, take an honest assessment of your community—its diversity and its overall health. Ask yourself: how much time a week do you spend connecting with others (outside of work)? Do you volunteer to support others or allow others to support you (both are good)? Do you feel enlivened or drained after being with those in your closer circle? Do you connect with people in your community with different beliefs than you? Don't overlook your basic need for community. As with good nutrition, good water, and good air, good community can increase your well-being. An unhealthy or a lack of community can deplete it.

## Habits

As we transform and grow, sometimes old patterns need to be allowed to die. This book might bring you to a few such places: as you practice truly inhabiting your body, you will begin to see with clarity ways in which you might be self-sabotaging. Nature demonstrates that it's okay to allow those parts that are not nourishing the system as a whole to wither and be composted to support future growth.

I think it's pretty hard to change your life without changing the system. But remember that letting go of something is a practice—a practice of not doing. Creating new habits or eliminating old ones is never a quick fix; these changes come one compassionate, consistent, and committed choice at a time. I can't tell you how many times I crashed and burned as I was trying to soar. But the important thing is to try, and if you fail, to try again.

Remember that most patterns and habits that we have developed, even "bad" habits, were developed to keep us safe or to cope with a challenge. Unhealthy eating habits, unhealthy relationships, and addictions of various kinds may all fall into this category. As you begin to let things go, allow yourself to honor the safety or comfort that these habits intended to provide. This honoring step can make it easier to release them. Some habits will be harder to change than others—the harder ones tend to be more ingrained, but greater freedom is on the other side. It's also important to note that the people around you might react to your growth or change—this can be challenging but keep going! Even positive change can be uncomfortable because it is new and unknown. Honor yourself with space and with compassion as you begin this journey.

I want to add a note about medication for anxiety, depression, and sleep. For some people, medication is very helpful, and for some, it is absolutely necessary. However, some people have been prescribed medications for stress and anxiety without being asked about past traumas or how they are tending to their mental, emotional, or spiritual selves. In this situation, the underlying distress has been robbed of the light of consciousness, a light that illuminates a path toward healing and integration. I have worked with a number of individuals who do not like how they feel while taking these types of medications; they feel as though a part of them is missing or is numbed out.

Through the work of reconnecting with their bodies and the restoration of their nervous systems by connecting with Nature, some are able to wean off their meds and feel more alive. If this is something that you want to address for yourself as you move through your practice, please go slowly and with the advice of a doctor. Everyone's situation is different and unique. Know that medicine in and of itself is not a bad thing. But also know that your body chemistry may change as you lower stress levels, and this change may eventually allow you to make new decisions about your needs for medicine. It's important to note that there is no escaping the wisdom of your body; it doesn't lie. Whether on medication or not, the body can't be bypassed. If you are carrying unintegrated or unresolved traumas, your body will call on you to do the work of healing.

Possibly the most toxic habit of all is self-deprecation. This is a habit that is relentlessly reinforced in our culture. "Not good enough" is a refrain that many of us practice, often unconsciously, and this detrimental habit holds us back from experiencing ourselves and life fully. Sometimes people say to me, "How can I give gratitude to myself? I cut myself down all the time!" Sadly, that sentiment is far from unusual. And that is why I'm going to recommend great vigilance in looking for all the sneaky ways this habit shows up. An important first step in becoming aware of the undercutting voice within your head is to slow down and be quiet. This is cultivated through the mindfulness practices in this book. Self-deprecating thoughts no longer have a hiding place in the contrasting light of Nature.

Once these thoughts are witnessed, you now have a choice—you can change the narrative. With practice and the reflection of Nature on who you truly are, you will form a new narrative, one that reflects your deepest, truest self.

## Commitment

An athlete doesn't become a champion right off the bench. They practice. And practice some more. If you want to reclaim your life, to reclaim your body, you will need to practice. There is definitely a level of determination involved. You've got to want to live a life that feels purposeful and connected because it takes work to get there. There are no shortcuts.

Before we get into the actual practices, make some space to get clear about why you are embarking on this journey. What is missing in your life? Is there a problem you are trying to solve? How do you want to feel? Spend a few minutes really envisioning this. The answers to these questions are what will keep you practicing when it gets tough.

In the next chapter, we will begin to practice. Please remember that even as you cultivate discipline, practice isn't about "have to" or "should." Look for natural opportunities to make them easy and enjoyable to do.

There are some simple habit hacks that can support you in keeping your commitment to yourself. For example, schedule your practice at the easiest time of day for you to be consistent; literally "write it in," as you would any commitment so that you are most likely to follow through. Choose a practice to begin with that will support you in how you have envisioned you want to feel. For instance, if you are seeking feelings of comfort and being soothed, you'd begin with a practice that matches that energy, such as the Cozy Spot practice in chapter six. Try connecting a practice with something you already do. For example, with your morning cup of coffee or tea, look out a window rather than looking at a screen. And voilà! You just completed your Nature Reset practice for the day. Always remember that compassion will get you much further than guilting yourself into doing something.

## Nourishment Practice

Let's jump right in and start nourishing! The following is a practice that will help you stay on track with nourishing the whole of you. With this practice, you are creating a menu of options to choose from that tend to your mind, emotions, body, and spirit. Your nourishment menu will be different than anyone else's—it is specific to you. The more you listen to your intuition and what deeply nourishes you, rather than what you are "supposed to do," the greater the benefit. You can create your nourishment menu at the beginning of the week or month and then decide on your level of commitment— do you select an item off the chart to nourish yourself daily or a specific number of times a week? It is up to you but do keep track. Seeing this commitment to yourself, specific and measurable, can be inspiring—it's how new habits are made!

1. Draw a box on a piece of paper and then draw a line both vertically and horizontally through the middle. You have now divided the box into four quadrants. If you find project apps helpful, such as Trello, you can create a board for each of the four quadrants rather than using paper. See chart on page 68.

2. Label each quadrant with Mind, Emotions, Spiritual, and Physical.

3. Before filling in your chart, take a few moments to pause and notice the rhythm of your inhalations and exhalations. Feel your feet on the ground and feel yourself settling in and being held by the spot you are sitting.

4. Within each quadrant, write one to three things you can do to nourish yourself in this area. Don't think too hard. Allow the act of nourishment to rise from within you. If you are feeling stuck around this, try journaling about what might nourish you. Make sure that your choice is attainable and try to hit the sweet spot of nourishment you can complete without strain or stress. No idea that rises naturally is too small.

Put this chart somewhere you can easily see throughout the week so that it won't be forgotten. Then take time to celebrate yourself at the end of the week for meeting your goal, entirely or even partially. Even if you completed two of the four, celebrate! You nourished yourself twice as much as you would have otherwise.

If you find the ideas aren't rising up, below are a few examples to jumpstart your menu. Nature has the potential to nourish all parts of ourselves with one practice. The next section has practices to support you no matter where you are or the amount of time you have.

**Emotionally:**
Connect with a friend, create music, garden, cook something delightful, get crafty, create a cozy moment

**Mentally:**
Read a good book, learn about something fascinating, memorize a lovely poem, meditate, nature brain break, solve a puzzle

**Spiritually:**
Choose a Nature practice (see next section), read poetry or spiritual writings, get lost in music, art, or dance

**Physically:**
Move your body joyfully (skip, walk briskly, dance, stretch like a cat), nourish yourself with fresh and unprocessed foods, sleep when you are tired, get bodywork such as a massage, bring herbal adaptogens into your life to help create balance

## Nourishment Practice

| MIND | EMOTIONS |
|---|---|
| | |
| SPIRITUAL | PHYSICAL |
| | |

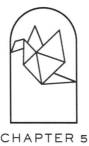

# foundational practices

From here, you are entering new territory. This guidebook becomes an interactive experiment where you try things you might never have before, give thought to ideas you might have considered "too out there," feel your body and emotions in new ways and conceive of a life that once seemed out of reach. You are now invited to make the switch from living as a brain-driven human to living as an embodied human. You do this through deliberate practice, and I am so excited to guide you each step of the way.

A few of these practices might be completely out of your comfort zone. However, as challenging as this first step might be, for many, your current comfort zone isn't so comfortable. But from here, no guru or teacher can pass on the wisdom you need. It is you, your feet on the earth, Nature as your guide, and your attention to your felt-awareness that leads you home. There's no way around doing it except to do it.

So, let's begin.

## Learning to be Subtle

One of the problems with modern living is that we've dulled our ability to feel things that are subtle. Much of the sensory information coming our way is overstimulating, so we end up tuning out a lot. When we do this, our perception of the subtle begins to diminish. However, much of the language of both the natural world and our bodies is subtle. To learn their lessons, we must awaken to this level of perception.

So how can someone who's not used to subtlety begin to feel these things or trust that they are there at all? The practices outlined in this chapter are intended to do just that—awaken your subtle perception. They are meant to be practiced regularly, like learning a new language. So, as you embark, know that a level of commitment on your part will be necessary—as with all things worth learning or gaining mastery.

As you know by now, I come from a scientific background. However, the ideas that I'm about to present don't always fit inside what modern science will permit. Suspending initial judgment is going to be part of your work. I invite you to come out and play with these practices! Let them awaken in you the kind of curiosity and wonder you felt as a child. An openness to experimenting is key, as experimentation is at the heart of all discovery. As you practice, you will become your own scientist—gathering data for yourself about how you feel. You are your own best verifier.

In this chapter, I present four basic foundations which become the cornerstones of your Nature Reset practice. These foundations are Nature, your body, your heart, and gratitude.

These are essential building blocks, and all subsequent practices are built upon them. This isn't a path of becoming someone else or even becoming a different version of yourself; these foundations are what allow you to become more fully who you already are. As you proceed, know that you will always be safe, and you will always be you.

## FOUNDATION 1: **Nature**

Nature brings people to a place of emotional openness. When I work with clients in a natural setting, we are surrounded by what is real and true. Being in Nature helps to "clear the clutter" so clients can unearth truth and wisdom around whatever they might be struggling with. Not only is this empowering, but there is also a reclamation of trust in their intuition and clarity for a way forward where they might have felt stuck before. You will find Nature holds space for your unfurling, for your reclamation journey of coming home.

For those of us who have put up walls of protection around our hearts, Nature is a safe space where we can gently and slowly take those walls down. Nature is an ally in your healing and personal growth.

Let me repeat that Nature doesn't have to be a pristine wilderness. Your backyard garden, or even a beloved view from a window, can be the most healing, magical place on earth. If it is a natural space that invites you to feel relaxed and in your true self, then it is Nature at her most nurturing.

### Nature-Based Mindfulness

Most of us have heard the term "mindfulness" and the phrase "present moment." These ideas are as beautiful as they are simple, but they are also so different from how we're taught to think, that many people find the concepts frustrating.

Here's a simple way to think about mindfulness: The mind is often like choppy water on a lake. Everything is stirred up. We sense a lot of movement but can't see anything below the surface. Once the water is calm, we can see down to the bottom, and that's when we become aware of the aliveness and depth under the water's surface.

When you're connecting with Nature, the choppy waters of the mind have a chance to calm, and you can experience the beauty and richness right in front of you with openness and curiosity—free of judgment. That is mindfulness.

Nature continuously calls us back to the present moment if we'd only pause to listen. That is why experiencing mindfulness, or a sense of the Now, is much easier outside. Every plant, every animal, and every element fully resides in the present moment. They are our mindfulness teachers.

Let's take a moment to imagine this. Picture yourself walking along a path, and you come upon some beautiful flowers. Instead of walking past them without noticing, commenting on them to a friend, or taking a picture of them and posting it—you simply gaze at them and allow their presence to create a moment of pause. The flowers remind you to feel your feet making contact with the earth, to be present in your body, and to open your senses. At that moment, thoughts that have nothing to do with flowers simply let go. And—you did it! That is mindfulness in action. It's not complicated: the flowers simply created a pause in the narrative. Your only role was to allow it to happen.

Sustained attention to the present moment wavers considerably for most of us. Past experiences or to-do lists will creep in, and in those moments, the sensory connection between your body and the natural world stops. But even that is okay. When the mind wanders, your work is to allow Nature to remind you to come back. As soon as you do, you will feel your feet on the ground; you will feel yourself taking each step; you will notice the flow of your breath; you will notice the wind on your skin, and voilà—you will experience the fullness of the moment again.

The more you practice this, the easier it becomes, and eventually, mindfulness will become something that you can practice no matter where you are. Normal things become extraordinary when they are done mindfully.

We can cook food with great intention and presence. We can absorb ourselves in listening to beautiful music. We can do everyday things with a little bit more sweetness. Step by step, your life philosophy becomes, "Let me show up to it," rather than "I'll just go through the motions." Everything you do is infused with the richness of intention.

## The Imaginal Plane

Nature embodies wisdom. When you allow Nature's inherent wisdom to truly hold you—as in feeling "held" by the stability of the earth rising up to meet you or "held" by a tree witnessing the authentic you—you will find yourself open and receptive to a greater mystery. This mystery represents wisdom beyond words. The poet Roger Housden says, "Poetry reaches with its sounds and rhythms down below the realm of the conscious mind to awaken and nourish the imagination." Nature, like poetry, invites us to enter into imagination. What I like to refer to as the imaginal plane. But in our culture, we've taught ourselves to block out that kind of thinking. We've been handed down a linear, logic-based way of being in the world, and it can take a lot of practice to undo that.

A good first step towards embracing mystery is to be curious. When we are actively curious, we feel a greater sense of aliveness because we are opening up to possibilities. We allow more than just the "naming" part of our brains to take part in the experience. When we have preconceived notions or we have already labeled something, we take away its mystery. Let's all be more curious about the things in life that can't be explained—releasing reflexive judgments. Entertain the idea that there is an inherent intelligence to everything—to fire, to wind, to the rocks, to all the plants, to all the animals. Just admitting the possibility of something more, something undefinable, allows for a subtle shift in consciousness.

Even if you're skeptical, consider for a moment your own experiences. Remember a time when you had a special experience in Nature. A time when something inside of you shifted, where you felt something greater than yourself, something that you couldn't explain with facts. Nature is much bigger than she seems, and much more complex than our human minds can comprehend.

*From that foundation of wisdom, we are going to find you a teacher!*

## Your Practice Partner

A "practice partner" is a part of Nature—a tree, a rock, a stream, etc.—that calls to you. This partner will be an anchor to the present moment, a trusted guide as your practice builds, and an ally in your personal growth.

What does a practice partner do? Let's walk through an example with an oak tree as our partner. An oak tree is a being whole unto themselves, not needing or expecting anything from you. The oak tree is in complete collaboration with the ecosystem in which they reside. They are supportive, open, and receptive, which equates to being non-judgmental. The oak tree has an inherent intelligence by their very existence and radiates their unique quality of being an oak tree out into the world. This oak shows up unconditionally as they become an ally in your unfurling of wounds from the past and holding sacred promises of the future.

Before you start looking around for the nearest oak tree, remember that Nature is everywhere! Your practice partner is going to be unique to you—and perhaps not what you first imagined. Perhaps a bush outside your office, a nearby pond, or a patch of ferns. All aspects of Nature are relational; you can't choose incorrectly. The important thing is a level of openness on your end. Decide that when you're with your practice partner, you will allow your heart to open and give yourself permission to be vulnerable.

When you choose a practice partner, approach them with reverence. Pause to ask them, out loud or in your mind, if they would be willing to be your practice partner. (You wouldn't walk up to another person and just start dating them! You'd at least introduce yourself, right?) Allow yourself to acknowledge that they have an innate intelligence beyond what your eyes can see. Pause and feel that. When you ask your practice partner's permission, you will usually get a yes. If you get a no, it might be because there are fire ants nearby or something else to be aware of! But usually, it's a yes because most aspects of Nature are giving and want to connect.

When you're with your practice partner, try dropping the label which they have been named. For example, if your practice partner is water, try to think of water in relation to properties, such as "one who flows." Taking off the label of "water" frees you to experience water's depth and vastness differently.

I once introduced a group of business professionals to a magnificent old cedar tree on a one-day retreat. I led them through the Heart Practice described below, and with the support of this beautiful tree, everyone in the group was able to experience moments beyond their senses of sight. Feelings, images, and awareness came forward. In some wisdom traditions, cedar is known as the grandmother tree, and one participant, unaware of this, experienced a great deal of peace as images of her recently passed grandmother came to mind. With a gentle shift in perception, we experienced what was there all along.

Sometimes your experience with your practice partner will be extraordinary, as that encounter was. But more often, your practice partner will probably feel like a deeply-grounding friend—the type of friend so comfortable in their own skin you feel braver and more yourself just by being in their presence. Your practice partner will be with you every step of your journey.

## FOUNDATION 2: **Your Body**

Feeling in your body is an essential aspect of mindfulness. Yet sometimes this foundation is overlooked or forgotten with a jump towards looking at "the mind." Some spiritual practices that seem to be anchored in mindfulness actually emphasize transcending the body. For me, embodiment is the crux of mindfulness.

I often use phrases like "feel yourself settling or landing in your body" or "taking a seat within yourself." It means occupying yourself fully, for example, feeling your feet making contact with the earth beneath you or hips as you are sitting in a chair. It's only from this state that you can really *feel* what is going on within your body. This often forgotten and very important sense is called interoception, and it is the basis of all of the practices in this book. Each practice says, not with words but with actions, "Okay, I'm going to be here now. I'm going to be in my body now."

The Body Practice that follows is the practice that all others are built on. In it, you will learn how to let your thoughts settle, how to let your energy drop, and how to find yourself in your center. Before I walk you through the practice, there are a few aspects I'd like to highlight.

### Breath

Slowing down the breath is essential for reclaiming your consciousness from the grips of stress. When we feel relaxed, the parasympathetic nervous system restores the body as it undoes the work of the sympathetic nervous system (the fight or flight response many of us spend much of our lives in). Slowing down your breath literally lets the rest of your body know you're okay. And when the body receives that signal, it allows itself to rest. Your breath is an anchor for the practices in this book.

Breath is your anchor to the present moment, no matter where you are. Therefore, with each practice, you are invited to give attention to your breath at the beginning and return your awareness to the breath if you find yourself distracted. Breath can be an integral and deeply enjoyable thing to notice, whether in these practices or on its own. The more you practice noticing and controlling your breath, the more you will be able to adjust your stress levels at any time.

## Your Feet

I don't think I've ever led a Nature experience without saying at the beginning, "Feel your feet on the earth." Not only do your feet help to ground you, but they are also a safe starting point as you work on feeling or "inhabiting" the rest of your body. Notice if this feels true for you.

Begin by feeling the subtle sensations in your feet: tingling, cold, or warmth. Next, try feeling the pressure of your feet making contact with the earth or the floor. Can you occupy your feet with your consciousness, feeling them not as appendages but as you. Notice what has shifted in your awareness as you inhabit your feet.

This practice might take time to master. Many people go from feeling nothing, to almost feeling something, to definitely feeling something. But the good news is, once you know how to feel your feet, they can help anchor and ground you wherever you are. From there, moving into the rest of your body is much easier. Your feet really are your friends!

**Tears**

When you start tuning into parts of yourselves that have long been ignored, this subtle waking up might evoke tears. The body stores emotions, and as you begin to tune back in, you can begin to heal and integrate strong emotions that you have carried. When I work with clients, it is not uncommon for tears to rise up as they feel their body. If you find tears rising up, remember that you don't have to think yourself through the healing: the healing happens at the level of the body. You might be releasing the frustrations of the day, but you also might be crying tears from your two-year-old self, and you will have no words for that. Just sit with the feeling, soften with it, and be with it—without judgment. If at any point you feel destabilized when doing this work, reach out for support rather than trying to navigate it alone. Being supported and witnessed by another person can be very valuable and healing.

## FOUNDATIONAL PRACTICE: **The Body Practice**

This practice will support you in inhabiting your body and experiencing the present moment—which is the first important step for all practices in section two and in showing up for life! I love this simple but powerful reset. It may take you a couple of minutes, but don't rush through it—allow yourself the time you need. Remember, the more you practice, the easier and quicker it becomes.

1.  We'll start with three intentional breaths to transition into the practice. Inhale through your nose for a count of four, pause, then slowly exhale through your mouth (or nose if you prefer) for a count of eight, then pause before inhaling. (Feel free to change the count, but have your exhale be longer than your inhale.). Return to your regular breathing rhythm of inhalation and exhalation through your nose. Check in with yourself. How do you feel? If you feel settled, continue to the next step, but continue to notice your breath through this practice. It is an anchor to the present moment. If, on the other hand, you have had a stressful day or you still feel tense, continue for a few more rounds.

2.  Bring your attention to your feet making contact with the earth (or the floor if you are inside). Feel the sensations in your feet (tingling, cool, warm, pressure). This is the felt-sense of having feet. Take up your space within your feet, fully occupying them—from toes to heel. It might be helpful to try one foot at a time and then feel them both at the same time. Feeling your feet helps to shift your attention from your thoughts to your body. You are "dropping in" to the moment.

3.  Now, bring your awareness to your hips*. While focusing on one hip, feel the subtle sensations in it. Inhale. As you exhale, send your breath to your hip with the intention of "settling into" your hip. Your breath will help to wake up this part of you, and it can heighten your ability to

feel sensations there. Repeat with the other hip. Now, feel the sensations of both hips simultaneously. Inhabit your hips. Take up your space within your pelvic area—your width as well as front to back. This is your place of power. Pause. Take a deeper inhale and longer exhale and rest here for a moment. *For those who have experienced sexual abuse, be gentle with yourself as you begin to reclaim this part of your body.*

4.  Now, you will turn your attention to your spine, very gently lengthening it. Imagine you are suspended by a string from the crown of your head. Gently align your shoulders with your hips. Shifting your posture in this way puts your body in an upright, open, and receptive position. With your breath and intention, allow your shoulders to soften and drop, letting go of tension.

5.  Bring your awareness to your shoulders. As you did with your hips, first feel the sensation of each shoulder individually and then inhabit them both simultaneously. Take up your space within your shoulders. Feel your width dimension. Feel your arms, all the way down to your hands. Allow your hands to relax and gently open. Pause. Take a deeper inhale and a longer exhale. Rest here for a moment.

6.  Bring your attention to your head. Soften the muscles in your jaw. Notice the area around your eyes and forehead and soften those muscles. Feel your breath moving in and out of your nose.

7.  Lastly, settle your awareness in your heart area. Feel sensations in the center, front, and back. Imagine resting and "taking your seat" here.

Your feet, hips, shoulders, and heart are anchor points to support you in "landing" in your body. Can you feel each of these anchor points at the same time? How about all parts of you at the same time, fully inhabiting your body? Can you feel the aliveness of your body?

You have just brought all parts of yourself "online" and enhanced your ability to receive nourishing sensory information from the natural world around you. The more you practice this, the easier and more fluid it becomes. Being in your body in this way can help you in seeing new possibilities, and new ways of being in the world, simply because you are fully showing up in the moment.

With this level of presence, you can show up authentically, with courage and compassion, to any situation. Try the above exercise before your next business meeting or important conversation. When you connect with others in this way, they feel your presence. And you will sense the difference, as your coworkers will feel seen, heard, and valued by you. This embodied state will also feel supportive to your loved ones— they will feel seen, heard, and valued. It will feel wonderful. That is medicine for any relationship.

For audio recordings, visit naturesoma.com/reset.

---

SPECIAL NOTE: **BE GENTLE**

Many of us have experienced trauma at some point in our lives. Unfortunately, years later, we can still carry those "'energetic memories'" within our bodies. Be gentle with yourself as you build body awareness. If an emotion or feeling arises that seems too much for you to handle on your own, move your body, become aware of your senses, and seek professional help for support. For some people with anxiety, feeling "aliveness" within themselves can be a trigger because of hyper-sensitive body awareness. Be gentle and move slowly. Over time, this practice will allow you to regain the knowledge that your body is a safe place to be.

## FOUNDATION 3: **Your Heart**

With a foundation of mindfulness in Nature and mindfulness in the body, we are able to experiment with making mindful connections outside of ourselves, as directed by the heart.

Have you ever connected deeply with the ocean—been moved by her? You might feel in awe, the relief of coming home, or deep gratitude rising as you stand next to the water. It causes a heightened state in your heart. At that moment, you have connected with the heart of the ocean. That is the feeling you'll be working with for the following practice as you connect your heart to that of your practice partner. When you first try out this practice, choose a practice partner in Nature that you already have an affinity with. The more you practice, the more your heart will unfurl and the more connection and goodness you will experience.

## FOUNDATIONAL PRACTICE: **The Heart Practice**

1. Bring your awareness to the area around your heart. Feel the sensations in the middle of this area, and also the front and the back. This is a gentle noticing, not an inspection or judgment about what you can or cannot feel. It might help to close your eyes so that you can put all your attention on what you are sensing in this area. Imagine breathing in and out through your heart on all sides.

2. If it feels supportive, on your next inhalation, set the intention for the area around your heart to soften and relax as you exhale.

3. Keep your attention and your felt-sense on the area in and around your heart. Then try to feel the following qualities in your heart, one at a time:
   - Spaciousness (the quality of openness)
   - Loving-kindness (the quality of warm-heartedness and goodness)
   - Gratitude (feelings of thankfulness for this moment)

Pause between feeling each of these qualities. When you resonate with one of them, you will feel that quality extending out from your heart. If you are having a hard time feeling a quality, reflect back to when you might have experienced it before and how your body responded. Can you bring that feeling to the present moment?

4. Now, intend to connect with your practice partner from your heart space. This is a felt-sense of your heart being open and witnessing the other. At this point, you are curious and open. Softening your gaze can help. Imagine your heart connecting with their "heart." For example, the heart of the ocean, the heart of a tree, or the heart of an animal companion. Breathe, relax, and allow your awareness and felt-sense to remain in your heart area. If you notice that you are starting to think, gently let it go. Allow your senses to help bring you back to the present moment. Drop back into awareness of your heart and the connection with your practice partner.

5. Allow the experience to unfold without trying too hard. Notice how your body and emotions are responding. The length of time that you stay in this connected state is up to you.

6. Conclude by offering gratitude to your practice partner.

For audio recordings, visit naturesoma.com/reset.

## FOUNDATION 4: **Gratitude**

We all know, it's nice to say thank you. That's common courtesy. But when you feel gratitude in your body, as you give and receive it—gratitude becomes a completely different experience. An open-hearted, embodied expression of gratitude becomes a shared experience; both the giver and receiver feel the gift of the moment.

In these practices, we begin and end with gratitude. We open our practices with gratitude because it supports us in getting to a flow state and it honors our practice partner. At the end of each practice, we intentionally pause in the heightened state that we created and acknowledge the worthiness of this moment and our partner.

I believe that any time we have a heightened state in our hearts towards something else or towards ourselves, a connection happens. If I've been listening deeply to the sound of a cicada, and I thank the cicada, either in my mind or out loud, I connect with that insect. There's a sweetness between us now. When we've enjoyed somebody's company, we say something like, "Oh, it was so good to be with you. Thank you for sharing time with me." Right? It's a closure. And if you feel the sincerity in your body, it deeply honors the other that you've connected with, whether they are a person, plant, animal, or the earth.

Gratitude is a state of mind that we can choose at any time. It creates internal shifts emotionally, physically, and mentally, and it allows for easy access to the heart. Even biofeedback equipment such as an fMRI can detect gratitude.

I can't overstate the power of feeling grateful to yourself, and I encourage you to do frequently. After you do the practices in this book, remember to thank yourself sincerely: "I did this. I'm doing this for myself because I am deeply worthy."

## Transcendence (a cautionary note)

If you're a person of a certain mindset, you will already be setting goals for yourself: I want to feel transcendence! I want to feel connected to the earth! But . . . I can't feel it yet. What's wrong with me? Am I doing this wrong?

I want to share some words of both wisdom and encouragement. Transcendence, or any form of spiritual perfection, is an enormous ask, one that I got lost in for years myself. I was always looking for a mountaintop experience, a truly elevated spiritual state. When I didn't feel that it was frustrating and disappointing. Perfection eluded me. I was chasing my tail, and it caused a lot of suffering.

Fortunately, one day, the demands that I was putting on myself turned into an "aha moment." I realized, all I need to do is settle into my body. What I was searching for was within me all along. It wasn't "out there"; it was "in here." I had been so distracted by seeking it kept me from where the treasure really was. Trust me; you will have a much easier time with these practices if you let go of spiritual "goals" and be here now, in your body, and in Nature. What you are actually seeking will unfold within and be reflected back to you.

I am excited for you to begin practicing! Remember that you don't have to feel like you are Buddha. You don't have to get these practices exactly "right" the first time. This is something that's going to evolve and develop in you because the wisdom teachings of Nature are endless. As you practice, you will learn how to be in your body and experience a profound connection with yourself and the world around you. In those moments, you will be home again! Welcome back.

....................................................................................................

....................................................................................................

....................................................................................................

....................................................................................................

....................................................................................................

....................................................................................................

....................................................................................................

....................................................................................................

....................................................................................................

....................................................................................................

....................................................................................................

....................................................................................................

....................................................................................................

....................................................................................................

 FIELD NOTES

SECTION TWO

# THE NATURE RESET PRACTICES

THE NATURE RESET

........................................................................................

........................................................................................

........................................................................................

........................................................................................

........................................................................................

........................................................................................

........................................................................................

........................................................................................

........................................................................................

........................................................................................

........................................................................................

........................................................................................

........................................................................................

........................................................................................

 FIELD NOTES

# the nature reset practices

Welcome to the practices! Here is where I share with you, step-by-step, the practices I have refined over many years. This is where Nature becomes your guide home. Through these experiences, you reclaim your inner landscape—restoration of your nervous system, rekindling of creativity and passion, return of flow both in body and spirit—and become rooted within. The foundations learned in section one will support you in experiencing the depth of each practice.

Each and every practice begins with embodiment—the foundational Body Practice described in chapter five. You start here in order to "land in your body" and connect to the present moment. This simple, intentional pause is what allows you to maximize the benefits of any practice. With that being said, feel free to substitute any embodiment practice in its place or change the Body Practices in a way that most supports you.

This chapter provides a roadmap to the practices. I begin by discussing "where and when," frequently asked questions, as well as some helpful hints to get you started. This is followed by a master chart listing all of the practices, their themes, suitable locations, and appropriate time to carve out for each practice. The chapters that follow contain these practices, grouped into themes of Nature Stillness, Water, Air, Nature Indoors, Neighborhood, and Adventure.

You may always go to a specific chapter to browse practices related to that theme, or you may return to the master chart to see all the practices in the book in one convenient location.

## Where Should I Practice?

Choosing a place to practice is important. It can be anywhere, inside or outside. Don't pick a place you think you should like; pick a place that actually feels good to you. The high-alert state that has become our daily experience is unsustainable, so your first priority is to find or even create a spot where you can feel safe and comfortable.

Remember that no matter where you are, Nature is always different, and untouched Nature is not necessarily better than cultivated Nature. For example, I recently conducted a mini-retreat at a bird sanctuary on a piece of land that has been well-loved for almost a hundred years. This land, which was reclaimed from a barren, over-farmed field, and lovingly cared for over years and years, is going to feel different than a wild space, but both are Nature, and both are beautiful. The bottom line is to pick a place in Nature that makes you feel good.

## When Should I Practice?

Any time of the day is a good time to practice. The most important part is to schedule it in, or life will make other plans for you. As you invite daily or weekly doses of Nature practices into your life, adding them to your calendar, just as you would an appointment, sets you up for success. If you don't, you may find slipping back to old patterns easier than moving on to new ones. This is something that I have to do for myself. For example, if I want to start my day with a practice, I take a minute to prepare the night before: I check the weather, lay out my clothes, know the spot in my backyard or within my house that I'm headed to, and plan in the amount of time I will dedicate to the practice. That way, I won't have to debate with myself the next morning if I'm going to do my practice because the hard parts will already be done. Without that tiny preparation, I could easily stay in bed for another fifteen minutes and miss the opportunity for a beneficial practice that could change the course of my day!

## How Long and Often Should I Practice?

These practices don't have massive time requirements; some of them only require five minutes. So, you could add a practice to the end of a run. You can even do some of these practices while taking a bath! If you are just getting started, five minutes might feel like the right amount. As you continue, extending the practice to thirty minutes might be just what is needed. Again, choose what feels good to you. On the master chart, I have listed recommended practice times. These are more about helping you plan, and they are flexible—use your intuition and the amount of time that you have. Some practice is better than no practice.

This is not about the quantity of practice, it's about the quality, and even more, it's about the regularity. It is much better to practice every day for five minutes than to practice once a month for two hours. That's why some of these practices are very short: if you practice every day, you're going to build new "muscle" much more quickly.

As I've experienced the benefits of daily Nature connection over time, I've come up with a term that many of my clients have found beneficial—microdosing Nature. Microdosing Nature is sipping from Nature's restorative cup, in small amounts of time, throughout the day. By the end of the day, you have experienced multiple micro-moments of restoration, which have a cumulative effect. But more importantly, you remember your connection and relationship with the natural world.

Many things you already do during your day can become a microdose Nature practice. For example, with intention, drinking a cup of coffee or tea can transform into a restorative experience (see Cup of Tea practice). Many of the practices I share in this section take what we do daily and turn them into healing and restorative Nature experiences. Since most of us do not live in the "wild," microdosing Nature can become a lifestyle or an adventure of looking for the next micro-moment to pause and connect with yourself and the more-than-human world.

Know that if you want to profoundly experience the transformation that Nature has to offer you, it becomes part of your life, like brushing your teeth. We're literally developing new neural pathways, and that takes repetition. As you proceed, inner resistance might arise, such as, "This is silly," I don't have time for this," or "This isn't important." Kindly tell those voices that those statements aren't correct. Tell them that, in fact, this is one of the most important things you can commit to and keep moving forward.

Know that when you first begin anything new, it might not feel as you expect—you might not feel much of anything, or it may be challenging. That's perfectly normal. You don't hop on a bike for the first time and start riding it. You're going to develop your skills over time. Remember that there is no perfection, and there is no endgame. This is about reclaiming yourself and your flow so that you can experience life the way that you want to experience it.

## What Does Setting an Intention Mean?

Your intention is like the needle on a compass that guides your practice. Each practice begins by setting your course. Setting an intention is not complicated. Just ask yourself: How do I want to feel at the end of this practice? The answer to that question is probably your intention! For example, you might want to let go of an intense office meeting or a disagreement.

You might want to feel more present and more still. Those are your intentions. Holding your intention lightly at the beginning of the practice will allow you to feel the difference in your body at the end. In addition, as your practice session unfolds, your intention might shift as you begin to settle in and become more aware of what is below the surface.

## Which Practice Should I Choose?

Not every practice in this field guide will resonate with everyone. I recommend that you read through the chart of practices first and then start with the one that is most interesting to you. Try it out. Go slowly. Take your time. You are learning how the practice works the first couple of times you do it, so try it more than once. The nuances and restorative effects will unfold the more you practice it.

Choosing a practice is a good way to take your own emotional temperature, so to speak. There isn't a hierarchy amongst these practices—they're all delightful. If you don't like bugs, look out the window and do the cup of tea practice. If you feel anxious, you might want to take a bath. In some seasons, you might find that you want to be still. In other seasons, you might want to be moving. Or sometimes, an element will call to you, such as water or air. You'll know.

Some of these practices ask for a certain level of stillness, and some people find it difficult to be still. Know that you don't have to be! You can slowly walk as you do most of these practices. Or you can look for a practice that involves moving. If you want to be still but feel too "revved up" to settle down, get your body moving for a few minutes—stretching, dancing, brisk walking—and then do your practice.

Aside from practical considerations, the main way that you choose which practice to do is through your intuition.

Land in your body and find your foundation for a few breaths (the Body Practice from section one). Next, settle into or feel your heart area for several breaths. And then, from your heart, look at the list of practices. At this moment, right now, what is the practice that you need? Which one has a pull on your heart? Find your "yes," and then start with that practice.

## HELPFUL TIP #1: **Successful Practice Overview**

- Choose the best practice for your lifestyle—considering space, time available, and ease of completion.
- Add the practice to your calendar and think through if there is anything you need to put in place to be prepared to follow through.
- Choose an achievable time goal—before your practice, set your timer and silence your phone or watch. This frees you from concerns of time and distractions.

## HELPFUL TIP #2: **The Flow of Each Practice**

This is a snapshot of the sequence of any of the practices from beginning to end.

- Acknowledge with gratitude your Nature practice partner.
- Set your intention.
- The Body Practice (pg. 79).
- The Nature Reset Practice you've chosen.
- End with gratitude and notice shifts in your mind, body, and spirit from the start of your practice.

## HELPFUL TIP #3: **Tune Your Practice to Sound**

Subtle medicine works best when we reset the mind, soften our bodies, and open ourselves up to receive. But sometimes, it's hard to get out of our own heads, particularly when we are feeling intense emotions.

I have found that sounds in Nature can often provide a quick way to shift from the mind into the body.

I know from experience that it is hard to find a space free of human-made noises, especially if we practice in suburban and urban areas. Choosing what to place your focus on can be a great asset. Rather than allowing your attention to be directed to human-made noises such as construction, cars, and yard equipment, place all your focus on a Nature sound. Perhaps a bird or the wind. Tune your heart into that direction as well, so the human sounds fade into the background and don't pull you in. If your urban landscape, office, or home space is void of natural sounds or too distracting with human sounds, listening to a soundscape can be beneficial. You can read more about this in the practice Nature-inspired Nest in Chapter Nine.

I'd like to share an example of how I've seen the energy of sound waves create space and open up constriction within one of my clients. I was working with this client at a park near my home. The sound of cicadas surrounded us, and their volume pulled our attention toward them. This was at a moment in our session when my client felt stuck and unsettled. Nature always provides just what is needed, and at this moment, it was apparent that she needed the cicadas. So, I invited her to receive the sound waves coming from the cicadas as though her body was a receiver. She softened her body and allowed the sound waves to land deeper and deeper within her. As she did, the vibration of the natural world began to create flow where she felt stuck, and a greater sense of inner freedom grew within her. She had started the day with pain in her heart, but the pain softened greatly as we received the medicine of the cicadas.

## HELPFUL TIP #4: **Tune Your Practice to Scent**

Stress and anxiety are being researched from all angles, including how they affect our sense of smell. Increased levels of stress can heighten the sense of smell. That's understandable from an ancestral perspective because the ability to sniff out dangers can sometimes mean the difference between life and death. As scent hits the limbic system, it affects our amygdala and hippocampus, and that response goes even more quickly to our brains than pain.

That is why scent can be a great asset to your practice. If you invite aromatherapy or pleasant smells in, you'll receive this sensory information quickly, thus making it an effective tool to down-regulate a hijacked amygdala or a fear response. Our brain and body get the memo saying: "Oh, it's all right. We're okay. This scent is good, so things must be settling down."

The indoor practices in chapter nine provide a great opportunity to use scent to quickly calm your nervous system down through essential oils or a cup of fragrant tea. When you are outdoors, stop and smell the roses (or wildflowers, mint, etc.). Try bringing your awareness to more subtle smells, as well, such as fresh air, pine needles, or salt water.

## HELPFUL TIP #5: **Feel Nature Feeling You**

All of Nature has an innate intelligence. If you allow yourself to feel that—you will sink into every one of these practices much more quickly. Begin in the imaginal plane—what would it feel like if, for example, the tree you directed your attention towards also directed their kind, gentle attention toward you? Can you allow yourself to be truly seen and witnessed by the tree? Allow yourself this imagination and see if it resonates.

Recently I was leading a college professor through some of these practices. She said to me, "I love plants! I'm absolutely a plant person. But I never thought about relating to a plant as I relate to a person, seeing intelligence within them. This changes everything." Once she pulled back the veil, she could see plants in a different way. It made her experience much more intimate, and she awakened an awareness and new way to connect with the more-than-human world that she now carries with her forever.

## HELPFUL TIP #6: Adapting for Children

Many of the practices in this book are adaptable to children and benefit them greatly. Sharing the sweetness of a Nature practice with a young person can be just as therapeutic to you as to them. Their tenderness, excitement, and curiosity are contagious and heartwarming. You may need to make minor adjustments, however. For example, when leading the Cup of Tea practice with a group of preschoolers, ensure the tea is warm and not hot. They will charm you with their exclamations of delight. I must add, with many practices, middle schoolers might roll their eyes, but without fail, they are always up for a cup of tea. Knowing your audience can be helpful for optimal engagement. The Cozy Spot practice is also a tried-and-true nourishing experience for children.

There is a philosophy in the Montessori world of "following the child." If you watch them, follow their natural desires, trust their innate curiosity, and follow their lead—practices can be adapted to support them individually, developmentally, and for that particular day. Resistance and frustration can happen when we have a preconceived notion of how things should be or if we try to fit them into a mold we conceived of even six months ago.

Children are constantly changing like Nature; we adults would serve them well by observing them and creating spaces that help them flourish. This isn't another activity. This is supporting them to remember who they are, to not be managed, and to just be themselves.

# Nature Reset Practices

| PRACTICE | LOCATION | TIME GUIDE | PAGE |
|---|---|---|---|
| **Cozy Spot**<br>Theme/Chapter:<br>**Nature Stillness** | backyard, patio, park, green space, blue space, wild space | 5-30 minutes | 104 |
| **Earthing/ Grounding**<br>Theme/Chapter:<br>**Nature Stillness** | direct contact with earth, concrete poured directly on earth, natural body of water | 10-30 minutes | 107 |
| **Entrain to Stillness**<br>Theme/Chapter:<br>**Nature Stillness** | green space, wild space, or rural backyard | 10-40 minutes | 109 |
| **Conversation with Nature— Fluid Journaling**<br>Theme/Chapter:<br>**Nature Stillness** | backyard, patio, park, green space, blue space, wild space | 5-20 minutes | 112 |
| **Night Sounds— a Remedy for Sleep Issues**<br>Theme/Chapter:<br>**Nature Stillness** | backyard, patio, park, green space, blue space, wild space | 5-30 minutes | 115 |
| **Flow Restoration**<br>Theme/Chapter:<br>**Water** | bath, shower, rain, or natural body of water | 5-15 minutes | 120 |
| **Blue Space**<br>Theme/Chapter:<br>**Water** | ocean, river, creek, pond, lake, wetland | 5-30 minutes | 123 |

# Nature Reset Practices

| PRACTICE | LOCATION | TIME GUIDE | PAGE |
|---|---|---|---|
| **A Cup of Tea**<br>Theme/Chapter:<br>**Water** | anywhere | 5-30 minutes | 125 |
| **Connecting with Air**<br>Theme/Chapter:<br>**Air** | anywhere | 5-10 minutes | 130 |
| **Breathing with a Tree/Plant**<br>Theme/Chapter:<br>**Air** | urban, suburban, backyard, park, green space, wild space | 5-10 minutes | 132 |
| **Feeling the Wind**<br>Theme/Chapter:<br>**Air** | urban, suburban, backyard, park, green space, blue space, wild space | 2-10 minutes | 134 |
| **Nature Inspired Nest—Creating Calm With Your Senses**<br>Theme/Chapter:<br>**Nature Indoors** | indoors | 5-30 minutes | 139 |
| **Indoor Nature Break**<br>Theme/Chapter:<br>**Nature Indoors** | indoors | 2-15 minutes | 144 |

Keep flowing onto the following pages for the
remaining Nature Reset Practices at a glance...

# Nature Reset Practices

| PRACTICE | LOCATION | TIME GUIDE | PAGE |
|---|---|---|---|
| **Eating with Intention** <br> *Theme/Chapter:* **Nature Indoors** | anywhere | 5-30 minutes | 146 |
| **Sweet Sipping of Cordials** <br> *Theme/Chapter:* **Nature Indoors** | anywhere | 10-30 minutes | 148 |
| **Elemental Embodiment** <br> *Theme/Chapter:* **Nature Indoors** | anywhere | 10-20 minutes | 150 |
| **Connected Walking** <br> *Theme/Chapter:* **Neighborhood** | anywhere walkable | 5-20 minutes | 158 |
| **Patio/Backyard Garden Cultivation** <br> *Theme/Chapter:* **Neighborhood** | backyard, patio, rooftop, balcony, window box, community garden | 10-30 minutes | 160 |
| **Crafting Cordials** <br> *Theme/Chapter:* **Neighborhood** | backyard, patio, rooftop, balcony, window box, community garden | 20-40 minutes | 164 |
| **Exercise Upleveled** <br> *Theme/Chapter:* **Neighborhood** | urban, suburban, backyard, park, green space, wild space | 5-20 minutes | 167 |

# Nature Reset Practices

| PRACTICE | LOCATION | TIME GUIDE | PAGE |
|---|---|---|---|
| **Forest or Nature Bathing**<br>*Theme/Chapter:*<br>**Adventure** | park,<br>green space,<br>wild space | 2+<br>hours | 172 |
| **Foraging**<br>*Theme/Chapter:*<br>**Adventure** | backyard, park,<br>green space,<br>wild space | 15+<br>minutes | 179 |
| **Retreating and Adventures in Nature**<br>*Theme/Chapter:*<br>**Adventure** | anywhere | one day<br>or multiple<br>days | 183 |
| **Guiding Kids in Nature**<br>*Theme/Chapter:*<br>**Adventure** | urban, suburban,<br>backyard, park,<br>green space,<br>wild space | 20-40<br>minutes | 189 |

For additional resources, visit naturesoma.com/reset.

FIELD NOTES

CHAPTER 6

# nature stillness practices

1. Cozy Spot  2. Earthing/Grounding  3. Entrain to Stillness
4. Fluid Journaling  5. Night Sounds

Nature Stillness Practices are all about creating a moment to pause from the busyness and just be. As you pause, Nature invites you to bring your whole self into the present moment and reminds you that you are part of Nature. Stillness practices invite you to settle into your body while allowing the stability of the earth to rise up to meet you. Without the distraction of movement, it can be easier to feel a sense of connection— the clay of your body connecting with the clay of the earth and your heart connecting with the natural world around you. These practices help you to know and simply say, "The earth is below me, Nature is with me, and I am here." Everything else is put on the shelf. This is deep, powerful restoration.

Through your senses, Nature gifts you with gentle nudges to be here now—supporting you in taking a break from thoughts of the past, future, and problem-solving. Examples of Nature's restorative cues include: What are you hearing, both close by and far away? What are the broad strokes and details of what you see? Notice the variety of the color palette before you. What movement catches your eye? Can you feel the trees near you without touching them? What subtle smells can you detect? You might look up at the clouds. You might feel the wind on your skin.

Eventually, your consciousness will move from your primary senses to noticing how your inner body is shifting and changing in response to the natural world and your own unfurling. The more you practice, the more you will settle in, and the more the light of your own consciousness will rise up. This is what it feels like to be home.

## PRACTICE 1: **Cozy Spot**

Take a break from doing and just be. With this practice, you will be "nesting" in a cozy spot—settling in, resting, delighting in, and being held by the natural world around you. This restorative practice relaxes your nervous system and guides you to feelings of calm, clarity, support, and safety.

When choosing your spot, you are looking for something that feels cozy, comfortable, and safe—so that you can unwind without feeling on guard. My cozy is different from your cozy; listen to your internal nudges as you look around for a spot. I love the base of a tree, and you might love a cozy chair on your porch. Preferably, you can return regularly to the spot you choose. You'll be surprised by how much it changes with each season, how much it changes you, and the enriching relationship you cultivate. A regular cozy spot is gold, but you might be on a hike, forest bathing, or on vacation and find the most wonderful tree to lean into—take the opportunity to experience such impromptu cozy spots when they call to you.

Remember, the intention of this practice is to pause, allow yourself to be held by the natural world, cozy in, experience stillness, and perhaps delight. This might be the most nourishing moment of your day as you unplug and unwind. The amount of time you commit to being in your cozy spot is up to you. If you find that you are having a hard time settling in, consider adding a weighted blanket to your cozy spot. Some folks find them super helpful in supporting relaxation.

**The practice:**

**1.** As you approach your cozy spot, pause, and imagine that you are placing your worries and burdens on the desk of a "universal manager." When placed there, some things will be taken care of without you having to make an effort. You might choose to pick them up after your practice or realize that they no longer need your attention. Throughout this practice, you allow nature to bring you back to the present moment through your senses so you can leave everything on the "desk."

**2.** Before sitting down, offer a heartfelt acknowledgment to this part of the natural world you will be joining—over time, you will come to realize how intrinsically connected you are.

**3.** Set your intention. Set a timer if you need to and settle into your body with the Body Practice (or any practice to feel your body). Allow your inhalation and exhalation through your nose to be soft and easy for the duration of the practice.

> Reminder: to set your intention, ask yourself:
> How do I want to feel at the end of this practice?

**4.** Feel the earth beneath you, supporting you, her energy rising up to meet you. Allow the pull of gravity to have its way with you as you settle into this spot and into your body. Sit or recline in whatever way feels most comfortable. Allow a quality of feeling heavy or dense—this is you getting grounded within yourself and letting go of tension. You are cozying into this spot, being held by the earth below you and the natural world around you.

**5.** Tune into your senses. They will support you in staying in the present moment. Receive each sensory input as if it is a gift.

Through these gifts, you are being supported and nurtured by the natural world around you:

- Can you feel the caress of the wind, the warmth of the sun, or the calming coolness?
- What sounds are making their way to you—can you delight in the bird's song or the rustling of wind through foliage?
- Are there subtle scents carried on the wind—what do they smell like?
- Do you notice the tapestry of colors and patterns around you?

**6.** As you are settling into the wisdom of your body, be curious about how it is subtly responding to the natural world around you. How does being among a diversity of life and natural elements make you feel?

**7.** Throughout this practice, use your intention, your senses, the felt sense of your body, your connection to the earth, and your breath to bring you back to the present moment. If you get distracted by thoughts, be gentle with yourself and allow your senses to guide you back to this moment of intentional coziness.

**8.** When you are complete, give gratitude for this time and all that you connected with. You can also offer a small giveaway, such as leaving some birdseed behind or singing a little tune.

## PRACTICE 2: **Earthing/Grounding**

Earthing, or grounding, is the simple practice of your body having direct contact with the earth's surface. There is no effort on your part except to take off your shoes or sit on the ground wearing non-synthetic material. Over time, the benefits of earthing, or grounding, have the potential to enhance your quality of sleep, reduce inflammation in the body, and enhance circulation.

The hypothesis behind earthing, or grounding, is that contact with the earth allows a free flow of electrons to enter your body and neutralize free radicals. Free radicals are atoms that have an unpaired electron, making them unstable. If an imbalance between free radicals and antioxidants arises, these unstable atoms have the potential to damage our cells and contribute to chronic inflammation, cancer, and other diseases. However, free radicals become stable once paired with an electron from an antioxidant or the earth.

Before the 1800s, every shoe sole was made out of natural materials, such as leather and jute. Up to that point, modern humans had direct contact with the earth for thousands of years. The invention of the rubber sole created an insulative layer between us and the earth. Between our time spent indoors and the insulation (of our shoes) from the earth, we have literally cut ourselves off from this free flow of electrons, gifts from the earth that help neutralize free radicals. And increased exposure to chemical pollutants and the consumption of alcohol and simple sugar have only created a greater imbalance. We need the support of the earth now more than ever.

Published research on the health benefits of direct contact with the earth includes decreased inflammation, reduction in stress, normalization of cortisol levels, improved sleep, and enhanced immune function, to name a few. We evolved as part of Nature, so it makes sense that we still require direct contact for our physical and psychological health and wellness.

Earthing, or grounding, is getting a lot of attention and is being researched in various fields. However, we are still learning what the optimal amount of time of contact should be. At this point, most recommendations are for twenty to thirty minutes. As in all things beneficial, it is better to do it, even for five minutes, than not to do it. You can add this practice to many others in this book for an added bonus, or if you have a particularly busy day, you can add this practice to something else that needs to be done, such as reading, writing, or catching up with a friend. Just do them in bare feet!

**The practice:**
Different ways to experience earthing/grounding

**Touch the earth.**
To receive the free flow of electrons from the earth, your feet or body need to be on a conductive surface in direct contact with the earth. The most effective is your bare feet, but you can also wear shoes with leather soles. If you choose to lie or sit on the earth, wear natural fibers like cotton or wool. Likewise, if you want something under you, choose a cloth made of natural fibers. Remember, materials such as a yoga mat are insulators and would not allow electrons to flow to you.

- If you think pesticides or herbicides have been applied where you are doing your practice, a cotton towel works well as a barrier.
- Damp surfaces are more conductive than dry ones—such as moist sand or grass covered with morning dew.
- Electrons can still flow through concrete if poured directly on the earth. Asphalt and wood surfaces are non-conductive, thus inhibiting the flow of electrons.

**Dig in the dirt.**
Gardening (without gloves on—if you wear gloves, make sure they are cotton) is a great way to be in contact with the earth. It also exposes you to a wonderful host of beneficial microbes.

**Touch a tree.**
A particularly sweet and nurturing way to ground! To sit with your back against a tree is a beautiful experience. Just make sure that you are wearing natural materials, not plastic-based polyesters, in order to experience the benefit of electrons flowing to you.

**Touch a natural body of water.**
Go float or stick your feet in a natural body of water. Let the flow of electrons in while your stress flows out.

## PRACTICE 3: Entrain to Stillness

Walking through the barren landscape one winter, I became acutely aware of the contrast between the stillness of the woods and what I was experiencing inside. This disparity highlighted my internal discomfort and unsettledness.

Longing for inner stillness, I stopped walking and found a seat beneath a majestic oak. Then, with my back leaned against her, I surrendered myself to the woodland's care. I let out a silent cry to the leafless hardwoods and the needled evergreens, asking for assistance to bring ease to the whirling dervishes in my mind, calmness to my frazzled nerves, and peace to my unsettled heart. I wanted everything within me to be still.

The whisper I received was to soften, let go, and allow the woods around me to entrain my inner landscape back to stillness. It was the first time the word entrain had ever come to me in Nature—and there could not have been a more perfect word. Entrainment is the process of something shifting to have the same rhythm or pattern as something else. In this case, I wanted to allow myself to be entrained to the stillness of the woods.

From my experience, entrainment happens when there is a gentle willingness on our part to soften and relax the body and allow the static of our current state to be felt but not attached to—to let it be. As you settle down, the static will as well. Sitting on the earth or leaning against a rock or tree can be helpful with this dance of you settling down and the rhythm of the forest settling into your bones.

For this practice, you need a spot that is more natural than human-made. The subtle energies of the natural world are the medicine for this practice, which can be overwhelmed and missed when competing with the human-made world. Greenspaces, botanical gardens, or woods work well for this practice. In addition, you should feel safe and free from distraction so you can let your guard down and deeply soften.

### The practice:

**1.** Acknowledge with gratitude the spot where you will be settling. Set your intention for practice, timer (if desired), and settle in your body with the Body Practice (or any practice to feel your body). Allow your inhalation and exhalation through your nose to be soft and easy for the duration of the practice.

**2.** For this practice, you can keep your eyes open or closed or shift between both. You will be working with the subtle and imaginal, and sometimes sight can get in the way of this. Notice if/how sight changes your experience.
- If your eyes are open, soften your gaze and the muscles around your eyes.
- Relax your forehead and jaw.
- Try a soft half smile, even if your heart is the furthest away from a smile; this will help you to settle and subtly shift your current state.

**3.** Invite your body to experience the quality of openness. Starting with the area around your heart, soften and invite the feelings/qualities of openness and spaciousness. Allow softness, openness, and spaciousness to extend to the rest of your core.

**4.** Now open yourself up to the subtle and imaginal. The natural area that you are in has a collective energy or vibration. All parts are coming together in an orchestra of subtle vibration, from the mycelium running underground to the lichen growing on trees. Imagine waves of this collective subtle energy moving into your body. Allow, soften, and receive. This is the entrainment part of the practice; you are coming into rhythm with the natural space you are in.

**5.** If you feel emotions rising, let them flow in whatever way they want to move. Try not to filter yourself. Stuck emotions or energy can cause us to feel unsettled at all levels—once they start to flow, it is like releasing a pressure valve; you will feel more settled and still on the inside.

**6.** Stay with this practice until you feel an internal shift. You might feel uncomfortable until the "pressure valve" is released; once it does, you will know. A feeling of calm, ease, and a sense of stillness will settle within you. If your time is limited, and you don't experience a shift, that is okay; you have benefited from this practice. Try again soon.

**7.** End your practice with gratitude to the natural area for the gift of vibrational medicine.

## PRACTICE 4: **A Conversation with Nature**

Do you feel stuck in a certain area of your life? Have you been searching for an answer to something, but it keeps eluding you? Are you wanting more depth to your spiritual practice—a direct line to spiritual insight? Or to deepen your relationship with the natural word? If it is yes to any of these, then this is the practice for you.

Nature reflects back to us what oftentimes we aren't able to see otherwise. It illuminates our blind spots, helps us to see ourselves in a truer light, and access wisdom that was there all along. With this practice, you are seeking connection, support, and/or clarity through "conversation" with an element in the natural world—for example, a tree, water, or horse, just like you would a trusted friend.

This conversation between you and the more-than-human world is facilitated by the process of fluid journaling. You ask a question and, from a heart-centered place, receive the answer. It is that simple. The crux move of this practice is not to filter any information. You write down everything that rises up—images, emotions, memories, words, awareness, sensations—all of it. The language of Nature is often subtle and sometimes surprising, and everyone receives this type of information differently. If it feels out of nowhere, you are on the right track!

As you write, try not to filter anything through the mind. Keep writing without stopping. The first minute or two might be at the surface level, which is why it is important to keep going. It's almost like clearing out the clutter to reach the hidden treasure —the unconscious. If you feel stuck, write that down or write out your question again. Set a timer for five minutes so you do not cut the process short. If you want your conversation to go longer, that's great too. After you are complete, you will read what you wrote and look for patterns or themes that stand out for you. I break down these steps below.

There are many creative ways to engage in a conversation with Nature. Are you missing a mother figure in your life? Tune into the strength and creative life force of Mother Earth right below you. At the ocean, imagine you are having a conversation with a loving, supportive mother. Allow questions and thoughts to arise, then listen. You can't get this wrong. The more you use your imagination and sense the presence of a loving mother, the easier your conversation will flow.

Have a conversation with any element of Nature that you are feeling drawn to. Perhaps even your beloved animal. I have led hundreds through this practice. The poetry and beauty shared after this experience often cause tears to rise because it resonates with such truth. Individuals are astounded by what is revealed to them. For most, they have never experienced anything like this. I'm excited for you to give it a try. This practice works well paired with the Cozy Spot or Forest Bathing practice.

**The practice:**

**1.** Choose your practice partner with care—one that you have a connection with, that catches your eye, or that you feel drawn to.

- As you approach, pause, and invite them to have a conversation with you. This ask inherently acknowledges that there is an innate intelligence to the one you are connecting with. It is a sign of respect.

**2.** Take your seat and settle in your body with the Body Practice (or any practice to feel your body). Notice your breath and allow your inhalation and exhalation through your nose to be soft and easy for the duration of the practice.

**3.** Imagine that your heart is connecting with the "heart" of your practice partner. For more on this, see the Heart Practice in chapter five.

**4.** Set a five-minute timer if you would like. With a journal in hand, ask your question, or ask what they would like to share with you. You can simply choose a phrase such as "This tree says..." or something similar.

Begin to write what is being shared with your heart.
- Let your writing go where it wants to. Don't filter or judge anything. It is all valid. The writing is moving through you; it's not coming from your mind.
- Write down everything that rises up—images, emotions, memories, words, an awareness, sensations.
- If you find yourself stopping, ask the question or a variation of it again. Keep doing this each time you find yourself getting stuck.

**5.** When your predetermined time is up, read what you wrote to yourself. You will be surprised by what is revealed to you. Look for patterns and symbols in your writing.
- Underline parts of your writing that stand out to you or moments of "aha." How does your highlighted writing connect?

**6.** When you are complete, give gratitude to your partner and their wisdom and the shared moment.

## PRACTICE 5: **Night Sounds Practice**

As the sun sinks in the west or the moon is at its apex overhead—this nighttime stillness practice is a sweet and relaxing way to get your daily dose of Nature, intentionally bring closure to your day, and reset your circadian rhythm. This can be very helpful as a go-to practice if it is dark when you go to work and darkness greets you on the way home, if it is too hot to go outside during the day, or if you just love being out at night.

Nighttime in the natural world has a very different rhythm than daytime. Photosynthesis stops, diurnal animals rest, the air cools as the sun goes down, and winds tend to calm. All of these subtle cues inform our body that it is time to rest and reset, which is the perfect message for our nervous system at the end of a busy day.

Many people aren't receiving Nature's message of winding down. Instead, they have disrupted circadian rhythms due to bright indoor lighting at night and artificial lighting during the day. This can affect melatonin levels in the body, interfering with sleep and resulting in mood disorders. Fortunately, research suggests that exposure to natural light cycles can counteract these effects and synchronize one's internal circadian clock. If you tend to have insomnia or sleep issues, this practice can be a powerful addition to good sleep hygiene. Commit to this practice for a couple of weeks, and notice a shift in your sleep quality and ease of falling asleep.

Before you head outside for this practice, I recommend dimming your indoor lights so that when you enter your home, the lights do not "reawaken" you. In addition, do not get back on a screen following this practice (before you go to bed), especially if you have sleep issues.

For those of you who live in the city, try listening to a nighttime soundscape while you soak in the night landscape. This practice can be done while sitting on your porch, rooftop, backyard, and even next to an open window with the indoor lights dimmed. As with all practice, make sure you choose a spot where you feel totally safe, relaxed, and at ease.

**The practice:**

**1.** For this practice, you can stand, sit, or lie down; the more comfortable you are, the better.

**2.** You can keep your eyes open or closed. If you choose to close your eyes, first orient yourself to the nighttime landscape. Gaze at the night sky and notice the various shades of darkness around you and the effect the moonlight has on the landscape.

**3.** Allow your body to soften and settle. With your intention, it will respond.

**4.** For a three-breath cycle, inhale deeply through your nose and exhale deeply through your mouth for a longer count. Allow the out breath to be an audible sigh if that feels supportive. This breath cycle is one of settling in, softening, and letting everything just be.

**5.** Sense the stability of the earth rising up to meet you. Soften the muscles in your forehead, around your eyes, jaw, and shoulders. The day is done; again, it is time just to be.

**6.** Allow gravity to have its way with you, supporting you in sinking and relaxing more deeply into your body.

**7.** Try honing in on one sound, and then expand your range of sounds to the level of receiving the sounds of an orchestra. Notice how your body responds.

**8.** Allow the sound or absence of sound to sweep the day's clutter from your mind.

**9.** Play with the imaginal and the feeling of your body. Can you allow the night sounds to reverberate within you, like the vibration of a guitar or piano string resonating, landing deep within? Allow the sound waves from the soundscape around you to settle in bone-deep. This will entrain you to the night and entrain you to sleep.

**10.** When you are complete, give gratitude to the creatures of the night, the elements that surround you, and yourself—for making time for you.

**11.** Once you have completed the night sound practice, try not to problem-solve or be productive. The day is done.

Now off to sleep with you.

...........................................................................................................

...........................................................................................................

...........................................................................................................

...........................................................................................................

...........................................................................................................

...........................................................................................................

...........................................................................................................

...........................................................................................................

...........................................................................................................

...........................................................................................................

...........................................................................................................

...........................................................................................................

...........................................................................................................

...........................................................................................................

 FIELD NOTES

# water practices

Have you ever watched a baby relaxing in a bath or children splashing joyfully in water? These sweet images are a glimpse of the medicine that water has to offer you—calming and restoring flow. Even as an adult, after a round of playing and swimming in the ocean, my body and spirit feel renewed. When leading retreats, if there is natural water flowing, I always invite participants to submerge. Without fail, we come out smiling and feeling a heightened sense of aliveness, especially if it is cold!

For ages, humans have had a beautiful relationship with water as we have asked water to bless, purify, baptize, heal, and cleanse. When approached with intention, presence, and gratitude, you can receive these gifts of water which are a healing balm to your body, mind, and spirit.

Aside from being essential for your body to function with fluidity and ease, water is also your masterful teacher on flow. Each of these practices with water creates an opportunity for you to reclaim flow in your body and learn water's wisdom.

Throughout the day, we have experiences with water, and each of them has the potential to be profound. The practices in this chapter are meant to transform ordinary experiences with water into extraordinary, nourishing moments. They are particularly helpful if you are feeling blocked, stagnant, or constricted emotionally, physically, spiritually, or mentally.

## PRACTICE 6: **Flow Restoration**

The systems in our bodies are designed to flow—circulatory, digestive, lymphatic, nervous, digestive, and urinary. It's important to realize our emotional "system" flows, as well. When one of these systems becomes stagnant, we experience discomfort and dis-ease. The focus of this practice is to restore flow to your emotions and mind—letting go of tension, repetitive thoughts, or stuck emotions. This, in turn, can actually improve the flow and functioning of your other body systems.

Water shares many endearing qualities: she can hold you up, gently caress your skin when falling upon you, speak to you through movement, and can be so beautiful and calming to look at in her different forms. With this practice, we invite all of these aspects of water to nourish your senses, emotions, and spirit.

Your intention as you practice is to show up as you are— stressed, vulnerable, tense, grieving, or wanting to experience the delight of a relationship with water. All are welcome—water has an inherent intelligence and doesn't judge. The more you can feel your body and stay with the sensations or emotions rising up—let them flow (or just be)—the more restorative this practice is. It takes a gentle willingness on your part, and the spirit of water does the rest.

This practice can be done in a bath, shower, rain, or natural body of water. If these aren't an option, a foot bath works, as well. I recommend trying this practice once a week, especially when things are going well. This will make it easier to call upon water when you are struggling, as it can be a challenge to start a new practice when we are feeling out of sorts. If you are taking a bath with the intention of clearing intense emotion, add one to two cups of Epsom salt and a few drops of lavender essential oil.

## The practice:

**1.** Set your intention for this practice and offer gratitude for water's support in restoring flow to your body, mind, and spirit.

**2.** As you enter the water, bring your attention to your body (a form of the Body Practice). Inhale through your nose for a count of four, then slowly exhale through your mouth for a count of eight. (Feel free to change the count but try to exhale longer than inhale).

- As you exhale, allow the muscles in your face and shoulders to relax, and gently let thoughts pass. Continue for a count of five breath cycles or longer if it feels supportive. Once complete, allow your inhalation and exhalation through your nose to be soft and easy for the duration of the practice.

**3.** Feel the water as it surrounds you or falls upon your body.

- If you are in the shower, and if comfortable, place the crown of your head directly under the shower head.
- If in the bath or body of water, if comfortable, submerge your head for a brief moment.
- As the water surrounds or pours over your ears and face, it increases your sensory experience, clears the mind, and brings your awareness to the present moment. It can also feel like you are being blessed as you begin this practice.

**4.** Notice if and where there is physical and emotional tension or constriction in your body.

- Suspend judgment or thoughts that arise related to the sensations you notice, keeping your awareness of what you are feeling in your body.

**5.** If you feel tension or constriction, gently direct your breath, along with an intention to soften and feelings of compassion, to the area of tension.

- Allow this part to be touched by the water and receive whatever quality of water it needs. Feel the water supporting you to relax, unfurl, and restore flow to this area.
- If it is helpful, you can imagine the spirit of water (choose any image or feeling—for example, mother ocean) supporting you.

**6.** If emotions rise, allow them to flow through you. This might be tears, a deep sigh, a sound, or a feeling of letting go. Stay with what you are feeling. When we feel uncomfortable, it is our natural coping mechanism to distract ourselves with thoughts, but this keeps us holding on to the tension or constriction.

**7.** Stay in the water until you feel complete, and then give gratitude to the water for supporting you.

**8.** Bring your attention to your body and make the transition out of the water slow and careful.

## PRACTICE 7: **Blue Space**

For many of us, a body of water has a magnetic quality. Water calls to us, and if we've been away from a natural body of water too long, we feel it and begin to long for our next encounter. Even if you're not a water person, this pull to be near water can emerge at different points in your life.

However, life gets busy, and it is easy to forget the deep nourishment that being next to water gifts you—that's where this practice comes in. It puts the need for nourishing blue spaces back on the radar so you can intentionally receive this medicine before your bucket dries up. It's also a reminder of how deeply healing being next to water can be. At times when I have struggled deeply, it's next to a body of water that my heartache has been gently tended to, and I've experienced an inner shift.

Have you ever watched a pebble drop in the water and followed its ripples outward until they reached the edge of motion and met stillness? It is this image that I invite into the blue space practice. The longer you sit with water, the more ripples and disturbances within you begin to settle. If you tune into water long enough, you create the opportunity to meet the edge of stillness within yourself. As feelings of calm settle in, it allows you to experience water in new and nourishing ways.

Water's messages are usually just what you need at the moment, particularly if you need support with something on your heart. Water calms the mind, helps the emotions flow, and tends to the spirit. Each body of water offers unique medicine and resonates with people differently. Is there a blue space that you are feeling particularly drawn to? This awareness is something worth listening to and responding to. Accept the invitation to schedule a "date" with you and that special blue space.

## The practice:

**1.** Begin to reclaim your internal flow by bringing your awareness to the rhythmic flow of your breath—gentle inhalations and exhalations through your nose. Notice the movement of breath in your body. With this practice, you can sit or stand, whatever is most comfortable for you.

**2.** Acknowledge with gratitude the blue space you are connecting with and state your intention—out loud or in your heart. Settle in your body with the Body Practice (or any practice to feel your body).

**3.** Make a few shoulder rolls, allowing them to release tension and soften. Slowly open your hands with palms facing up or touching the earth. If you feel unsettled, rest your open hands face down, on your thighs to begin with.

**4.** Feel the area around your heart—the front, back, and center. Take a breath in and as you exhale, rest here, and let your awareness and energy settle in your heart. This is a sweet moment for the Heart Practice in chapter five. Connect with the water from your heart.
- Try softening your gaze while looking at the body of water; relax your forehead and the muscles around your eyes.

**5.** What aspect of the blue space is drawing your attention? Rest your focus and attention here. How does your body respond? If there is a message here for you, allow it to arise without mental strain.

**6.** Continue to soften, staying present to subtle shifts within the blue space and within you.
- Let all of this awareness help you settle deeper into a state of calm, reclaiming your flow and centeredness.

**7.** When you feel complete with this practice, give gratitude to the blue space for the connection and restoration you received.

## PRACTICE 8: **A Cup of Tea**

Drinking a cup of tea is a tradition that has been shared within myriad cultures for time immemorial. We drink a cup of tea to warm up or to connect with friends. We enjoy tea as a way to relax and unwind. In forest bathing, we often share tea made from foraged herbs. One of my friends and colleagues, who is from Ireland, has her afternoon tea without fail. Simply witnessing her taking a teatime evokes a feeling of relaxation and ease in me!

The commonality in all tea-drinking experiences is that tea represents a break from ordinary life—we take a certain amount of time away from the "normal" to allow the tea to nourish us on all levels. Envision hands wrapped around a warm mug as steam rises to meet the relaxed-looking recipient—it's an image we have all seen or experienced. This moment of restoration is the "why" behind this practice—whether you are in the middle of a busy office or out in the wilderness.

The full sensory experience—the warmth of a mug in your hands, the steam rising to meet you, the smell of aromatic herbs, the awakening of your taste buds—brings the magic to this practice, even on the sixtieth floor in the heart of a city. Besides the restorative aspects of this practice, it is relational—an opportunity to experience the subtle sweetness of connecting with a plant. Are you interested in an experience with lavender, lemon balm, or peppermint, for example? I've listed some recommendations below and invite you to take a moment to find out what the plant looks like and where they grow if you are unfamiliar with them. This curiosity will support you in connecting to the plant and receiving their medicine.

Try practicing with one herb at a time so that you can experience each herb's unique qualities and develop a relationship with them. There is also a special magic in herbal blends, as you can imagine being part of this sweet community.

As with all medicinal herbs, make sure they are organically grown, and please check to see if there are any contraindications for your current health conditions.

The act of tea-making is an integral part of the practice. Be intentional as you select your herbs and mindful as you pour the water over the tea leaves or flowers. If using dried herbs in a tea bag or tea ball, steep about one teaspoon per cup of water for five to fifteen minutes. Feel free to adjust the amount of herb you use, depending on your preference. For fresh herbs, fill a tea ball and steep for the same amount of time. A clay mug is nice for this practice as it radiates warmth.

### The practice:

**1.** Once you have your tea prepared, set your intention. Are you wanting to relax? If so, maybe say to yourself, "I am giving myself this moment to slow down and unwind." Do you feel stuck or stagnant? As with all water practices, this one helps to restore flow. Simply ask for the water and herbs to flow to places that need softening and opening.

**2.** Settle in your body with the Body Practice (or any practice to feel your body), and allow your inhalation and exhalation through your nose to be soft and easy for the duration of the practice.
  • If you are seated, allow yourself to "sink in" and be held and supported by what is underneath you.

**3.** See this cup of tea for what it truly is—more than just liquid. It was kissed by the sun, nourished by the earth, experienced the change of seasons, and swayed in a field with the wind. You are taking all this in and being nourished. Allow this to help you cultivate gratitude for the plant(s) in your tea.

**4.** As you hold your cup, feel its warmth radiate into your hands, up into your arms and flow toward your heart.

**5.** Breathe in the aromatics of this plant and feel the steam caress your face.

- Notice how your body responds. Allow your body to relax and settle with each slow sip.

**6.** Bring your awareness to your heart area, and envision a sense of openness and compassion here.

**7.** As you drink your tea, invite the plant's spirit to join you in this experience, just as you would invite a friend. Perhaps see the plant with your mind's eye. Whatever image comes up is just the right one. (You might have a feeling of connection rather than seeing.)

**8.** As you drink your tea, if you feel yourself becoming distracted, return to where you started. Notice your breath. Notice your senses as they are being stimulated by the tea. Notice the felt sense of aliveness within your body. Notice the qualities of openness and compassion within your heart. Stay open to receiving. The plant that you have chosen for your tea has real gifts to offer your mind, body, and spirit. Stay present so that you can experience them.

**9.** When you are complete, give gratitude to yourself for carving out this restorative time. Give gratitude to the plant's spirit for helping you.

**10.** As a final gesture of gratitude, let your tea leaves enter back into the cycle of life. Composting or returning the tea leaves to Nature, next to a tree or plant, is the most honoring practice.

On the following page is a list of some of my favorite herbal teas to consider for this practice, but you are by no means limited to these. There are many wonderful plants to connect with. Most of these herbs are easy to grow or forage for. Cultivating and foraging for herbs adds another level of therapeutic Nature connection. (See Patio/Backyard Garden Cultivation on pg. 160 and Foraging on pg. 179)

As a side note, a cup of tea is different from a medicinal infusion, in which you steep the herbs for hours. That being said, chamomile and jasmine tea are of medicinal strength with five minutes of steeping.

## Delightful Herbal Teas for Connection and Emotional Support

| PLANT | EMOTIONAL SUPPORT | CULTIVATION/FORAGING NOTES |
|---|---|---|
| **Lemon balm** *leaves* | calms the heart and body; stress relief; supports nervous system | cultivate in a contained area (they spread); indoors in south-facing window |
| **Chamomile** *flowers* | calms and supports nervous system (especially a nervous stomach); sleep aid | cultivate in a garden or container outside |
| **Violet** *leaves* | calms the heart, grief and heartache | forage in your backyard or wild places; add to salads or sandwiches |
| **Lavender** *flowers* | relieves tension, stress, anxiety; depression support, uplifting; sleep aid | cultivate as part of landscaping or garden—must have well drained soil |
| **Holy basil (tulsi)** *leaves* | antidepressant, adrenal support, helps with fatigue and stress | cultivate in garden or part of landscape |
| **Rose** *flowers* | inspires self-love; healing after betrayal or death of loved one | cultivate in garden or part of landscape |
| **Nettles** *leaves* | tonic for the whole body; rich in vitamins and minerals, nourishes the nervous system | cultivate in a contained area (they spread) or forage in the wild – must use gloves to handle until you cook or dry, as they sting; also use as substitute for spinach in cooked dishes. |
| **Peppermint** *leaves* | reduces stress; anxiety relief; calming and uplifting effect | cultivate in a contained area (they spread); indoors in south-facing window |

CHAPTER 8

# air practices

9. Connecting with the Air  10. Breathing with a Tree or Plant
11. Feeling the Wind

The classic movie Mary Poppins begins on a windy day as nannies are being blown off the front stoop of a family's house. It makes you chuckle, but pause for a moment and think about the power of that. Wind cleared the stoop and brought an agent of change, Mary Poppins! When peace and balance were restored, she flew off with the winds that brought her. The story ends with the family skipping down the road, kites in hand, as the wind dances around them. Wind brought the Banks family the openness to see with fresh eyes, the rekindling of play and wonder, and the hope of new possibilities.

Openness, awakening, and new possibilities are the gifts and medicine of the element of Air. There is an intimacy to air. Its movement caresses our skin. Its coolness sweeping across our skin can cause hairs to stand on end. When it holds moisture and heat—it causes us to strip down to the bare minimum. The scent it carries can calm or bring the message to stay alert. Each of us has a relationship with the air, as it has surrounded us since birth.

The breath, your invitation for air to dance within you, is an anchor to the present moment and the foundation for movement practices ranging from yoga to Qigong. Focusing on your breath is a simple but powerful act. It can stimulate the feeling of aliveness within your body. Your breath can help ease pain, move emotional blocks, release tension, and recenter you during times of stress. With each breath, you are rekindling an ancient partnership with the element of Air, and you realize you are never alone.

With each of the following practices, you are invited to experience the subtlety and strength of the element of Air—the swaying treetops, its wind dancing across your skin, and the subtle scents it offers you. Each of these experiences beckons your awareness to rest within your body and the present moment. As wind comes to meet you and caresses your skin, it supports you in awakening from feeling numb and disconnected. Through these practices, you will notice the air around you and within you and tap into its restorative power.

## PRACTICE 9: Connecting with Air

Each breath we take is an invitation for air to flow into our bodies and nourish us. Just watch a baby or furry friend as they sleep—it looks as though they are inviting air into their whole body with each breath. Their bodies gently rise and release as air dances within them and then takes leave, and it's this image that we carry into this practice.

With this practice, we are reinvigorating our relationship with air. Yes, we breathe in and out all the time, but for the most part, we take this relationship for granted. However, in moments when we step into new landscapes, such as taking in the crisp morning mountain air or after a storm has blown through and cleared away smog and pollutants—we remember the sweetness of the air and our connection with it.

Metaphors allude to the qualities we associate with air: we open a window to "freshen" a room, we "breathe new life" into projects by offering new perspectives, and we might have a challenging conversation with someone so we can "clear the air" and create space for the relationship to move forward. With this practice, we invite these qualities of new beginnings, a fresh start, and creating spaciousness within ourselves.

In addition, I invite you to play in the imaginal during this practice. Try removing the label of "air" from your thoughts. This word seems limiting to one who always surrounds us and sustains our lives. Take a moment to imagine the air you're breathing in at this moment as dancing within your inner landscape—just like the wind dances as it swirls through prairie grass. During this practice, you turn what might be perceived as an ordinary moment into an extraordinary one. And it's one that can be done anywhere! If you can get outside, great; if not, try standing by a window. In less than five minutes, you receive the benefits of restoration and connection. Intention setting and the Body Practice are integrated into the practice seamlessly.

### The practice:

**1.** Notice your feet making a connection with the earth—lengthen your spine and lower your shoulders with the intention to relax and let go.
- Notice your breath. Allow your inhalation and exhalation through your nose to be soft, easy, and without pause – allow the air to flow in and out.

**2.** First, simply feel your skin making contact with the air. Feel the quality of air – its temperature, moisture, and movement.
- Try to feel the air surrounding you in a sweet, nourishing way, as though you are being lightly held or hugged.

**3.** With your next inhalation, intentionally invite the element of air into your body, bringing with it the qualities of spaciousness, openness, and new beginnings.
  • Feel these qualities within your core.

**4.** For the next few breaths, as you inhale, imagine you are receiving life force energy (or chi—whatever term works best for you) and nourishing each cell in the front of your body and relaxing as you exhale. Notice how your body responds.

**5.** Continue with this same intention but focus your breathing on your backside and then the side body. Notice how these different parts respond.

**6.** Now, breathe with the whole body. Notice places that feel stuck on a physical level or on an emotional level. Ask air to ease tension, restriction, and to restore fluidity to your body.

**7.** When your practice time is over, take a moment to feel the changes in your body. Then offer gratitude to the air for the gifts you received through this connection.

## PRACTICE 10: **Breathing with a Tree or Plant**

Breathing in the breath of another. Sounds pretty intimate— which is exactly the type of experience this practice has the potential to be. You and a plant—exchanging breaths in a moment of connection.

By breathing in, you receive the tangible gift of oxygen; however, there is more to this practice than just taking in valuable molecules. The sensuality of this practice comes from being in your body (see chapter five: The Body Practice) and "taking in" the other as you give part of yourself to them. With your inhalation, you take in the sweetness, vitality, beauty, and authenticity of your practice partner, and you share the same with them on your exhalation.

We do this rhythmically with breath. Giving and receiving—a dance of reciprocity.

This is an opportunity to have the outer landscape literally come into your body and travel throughout it. Allow your body to be moved by this sacred encounter. This practice will remind you of your primal interconnection with the natural world in a visceral way.

Through our exhalations, we offer the gift of carbon dioxide to plants and trees. However, human activities now produce an abundance of this molecule in so many different ways that it is no longer a gift. Protection, nurturing, and tending to are potent gifts we have to offer in gratitude for the oxygen we receive.

This practice can be done anywhere: a bush outside your office, a tree in your yard, or a plant in a local park. Before beginning, select a practice partner (review Your Practice Partners in chapter five if you don't know what that is) and honor them by inviting them into this practice with you.

The time commitment to this practice is minimal. Commit to five minutes, but you might want to increase the time because it feels so good.

**The practice:**

**1.** As you are standing or sitting next to your practice partner, "land" in your body so you can join them fully, as they are completely inhabiting themselves. (The Body Practice— chapter five).

**2.** Slowing your breath down for this practice is helpful. Try inhaling through your nose for a count of five and then exhaling for a count of five. Maintain this rhythmic breathing for a few rounds of breath.

**3.** Next, with the same slow and intentional breath, imagine you are breathing with your heart—as you breathe in, energy and vitality are flowing in. As you exhale, energy and vitality flow or radiate out as if your heart is the center point of a star.

**4.** With continued awareness of the area around your heart, feel the qualities of spaciousness, loving-kindness, and gratitude within you.

**5.** Now extend these qualities to your practice partner. Remain in this sweet place of connection for the duration of this practice. What do you notice?

**6.** Begin consciously breathing with your partner. Receiving on the inhalation and giving on the exhalation. There is no effort needed, nothing to think about, just you and your practice partner in communion with each other. Feel your body and heart and notice what shifts.

**7.** When you feel your practice is complete, pause, really see your practice partner with your heart, and offer them gratitude.

## PRACTICE 11: **Feeling the Wind**

Wind catching the hair of a heroine or hero and tossing it about with wild abandon is a classic movie shot. This scene evokes personal freedom, strength, and a taste of the untamed. Wind can create an inner stirring—rekindling a sense of aliveness and helping free what feels stuck. You are awakened to these qualities as a gentle breeze sweeps across your face or dances through the trees.

Some folks are wind people, and I'm one of them—I love the wind. When I re-introduce groups to the idea of connecting with the wind, some people light up with remembrance. There is an internal shifting within them, and I'll hear something like, "Oh, I have forgotten how much I love the wind!"

Their relationship with wind, perhaps forgotten since childhood, is rekindled. Wind becomes an ally again—inviting wild, creative, and untamed parts to come out and play. Wind invites us to pause and delight in the moment.

Wind also offers the special gift of clearing the air. When connecting with the wind, as you would with the ocean or a tree, you can ask for its subtle medicine to clear the energy around you and move what feels stuck within. As you soften your body and invite wind to blow through and all around you, you may feel clear and calm, like the air after a storm blows through.

I want to acknowledge, though, that not all people have a positive relationship with wind. If you live in an area prone to tornadoes, wind might be uncomfortable at best and even cause fear. With extreme climatic events on the rise, wind is speaking up like the rest of the earth, letting us know of the earth's imbalance. If you would like to experience a different relationship with the wind, a breezy day might be a good place to start.

This practice can take just a moment, as in pausing and fully feeling a gust of wind. If you are drawn to this practice, keep it in your back pocket for a windy day. If you've been going through the doldrums, nothing is as refreshing as new wind blowing.

With this practice, whatever part of your body is exposed is enough. Even if you are covered, you are surrounded by the wind and its energy. Choose your spot based on conditions; if the wind is blowing hard, avoid woodlands or standing under trees, as limbs can fall during gusts. This practice is also lovely paired with the following practices: Forest Bathing, Cozy Spot, or Exercise Up-leveled.

**The practice:**

**1.** Set your intention and settle in your body with the Body Practice (or any practice to feel your body). Allow your inhalation and exhalation through your nose to be soft and easy for the duration of the practice.

**2.** Feel the earth beneath your feet. Imagine you are strongly rooted as a tree through your feet and allow the rest of your body to feel the flexibility of a tree yielding and moving with the wind.

**3.** Feel the wind on your skin and its changes in movement and temperature. See it blowing the plants and trees.

**4.** Feel the area around your heart—the front, back, and center. Take a breath in and as you exhale, rest here, and let your awareness and energy settle in your heart. Connect with the wind from your heart (see Heart Practice in chapter five). You are connecting with the spirit of wind—playing with the imaginal can help with this.

**5.** Feel your body and reflect back on your intention. Was it to feel free? Unstuck? Delight in the moment? A return of vitality? Or to receive wisdom from the wind? From your heart, communicate this with the wind—or simply just be with the wind.

**6.** As you are connected with the wind, notice what is shifting within your body. It might be very subtle. Can you feel yourself being solid and strong but also with the flexibility to bend and yield?

**7.** When you are complete with your practice, give a heartfelt thank you to the wind for being with you and supporting you.

# indoor nature practices

Sometimes, getting outside is not an option, but that doesn't have to stop you from getting a much-needed dose of Nature. Feeling foggy-headed after a long meeting, but you've got to keep going? Looking out the window at a tree or blue sky for just 40 seconds has a restorative effect on cognitive function. Perhaps you are stuck inside due to illness or injury. A window view of Nature can decrease recovery time and even reduce the need for strong analgesic medications. These are just two examples of scientifically-backed benefits of connecting with Nature from the indoors.

Throughout this guide, you are invited to expand your concept of what Nature is to include the subtle ways she shows up in suburban and urban environments. With indoor Nature practices, we broaden our scope even further to include window views, aspects of Nature that we bring indoors and fuse into our built environment, and our relationships with the plants we eat.

Many of the practices within this chapter are microdose Nature experiences that are meant to nourish and sustain you until you can get outside. It's not that these are "less than" practices; they are just different.

They are all anchored by settling into your body and cultivating awareness of your breath, so practicing them will enhance your outdoor practices because you will be able to settle into your body with greater ease.

Have you noticed how indoor spaces can sometimes cultivate an atmosphere of stress? Within the modern workplace, for example, we don't have lions chasing us, but we do have the pressure of a boss, deadlines, and a host of other "perceived" dangers. No wonder so many of us have frazzled nerves. Our systems are often on alert, but we are literally stuck behind a computer. Lots of pent-up energy with nowhere to go.

Weaving micro-moments of Nature experiences into your day at the office or home can be an effective way of communicating to your nervous system that you are okay—"these are minor annoyances, not true threats, you are okay." A Nature pause supports you to recenter, refocus, and restore. Yes, most of us would prefer to be walking in the woods or wandering in wild spaces—but busy schedules, inclement weather, illness, or physical limitations don't have to be barriers to getting Nature nourishment.

Before starting an indoor practice, I highly recommend doing a few seconds of gentle movement, such as: rolling your shoulders, shaking your legs and arms, or doing a few spinal twists. This will help get your blood, lymph, and energy flowing—making it easier to transition into practice and to help you feel your body. After gentle movement, settle into the moment with the Body Practice (chapter five), then proceed to your indoor practice.

## PRACTICE 12: **Nature-inspired Nest**

Creating a calm sensory Nature-inspired nest, whether at home or your office, can be just the medicine your nervous system needs during a busy day. Think of the host of calm sensory experiences you receive when out in Nature—imagine bringing that indoors. The scents, sounds, tastes, colors, patterns, and elements of the natural world can be woven into your indoor landscape or pulled out from an office drawer to create an intentional break or microdose Nature experience.

With this practice, you are not redesigning your house, though biophilic-designed spaces are amazing! You are creating a spot, or a nest, to return to again and again. With your go-to nest created, you'll easily be able to step away when you need a brain break, need to hit the emotional pause button, or just need a little sensory lift.

Below are some recommendations to include in your nest or in a drawer for a pop-up nest to naturally support a sense of calm indoors. Have fun picking and choosing elements that appeal to you. The treasures in your nest will also be helpful for the next practice—the Indoor Nature Break.

### Smell

Scent has the power to quickly shift your state, and the therapeutic use of aromatic natural oils has a rich history dating back thousands of years. This practice is about bringing the outdoors in by stimulating your sense of smell with natural essential oils—it is simple, yet powerful.

Our attraction to scent is undeniable but also quite personal as to likes and dislikes. When choosing a scent, notice how your body responds to it. Select a scent where you notice a positive response physically or emotionally.

Does the scent cause you to feel relaxed or uplifted? You can also try making your own blends. The following chart offers examples of essential oils that give you the sense of being in Nature and support your emotional well-being.

As a side note, essential oils are potent and should not be taken internally (unless under the direction of a medical professional). If you apply them to your skin, they should be diluted in a carrier oil such as jojoba, olive, or coconut. For most adults, a two percent dilution rate is recommended. For example, you would use four to six drops of essential oil in two teaspoons (ten milliliter) of carrier oil.

**Ways to stimulate your sense of smell:**
- Diffuse an essential oil into the air. For a 100 ml diffuser, use three to five drops of essential oils. You can use a single oil or blend different ones.
- Massage diluted (see above) essential oils into your wrists or palms and inhale deeply. This practice is a good choice if you share a space with others who may not have similar scent preferences.
- Place a couple of drops of essential oil on a tissue and take a few deep breaths. This practice is also helpful if you share a space.
- Put a cotton ball with drops of essential oil in a small glass jar. You can open and take a few sniffs when desired without the scent entering the larger environment.

# Essential Oils

| ESSENTIAL OIL | EMOTIONAL SUPPORT | BLENDS WELL WITH |
| --- | --- | --- |
| **Cedarwood** | sedative action; soothes anxiety, grounding | bergamot, cypress, juniper, rosemary |
| **Cypress** | refreshing action; relaxing, supports circulation | bergamot, clary sage, juniper |
| **Juniper** | stimulating action; counteracts depression and fatigue | bergamot, cypress, geranium, rosemary |
| **Pine** | uplifting action; refreshing | cedarwood, rosemary |
| **Rosemary** | invigorating action; counters fatigue, helps with circulation and headaches | cedarwood |
| **Geranium** | relaxing action; refreshing, supports nervous system | any oil |
| **Clary Sage** | soothing action; nerve tonic, counters depression, relieves insomnia | bergamot, cedarwood, cypress, geranium, juniper |
| **Bergamot** | uplifting action; refreshing, soothes anxiety and depression | cypress, geranium |

## Sound

Nature sounds have been found to support mood recovery after experiencing a stressor. After your next intense interaction, try putting on a Nature soundscape that is calming to you, such as the ocean, and close your eyes, slow your breath, and just listen for a couple of minutes. This will give your body, mind, and emotions a space to reset.

If you live or work in an area with a surplus of human-made sounds, try changing your sound backdrop to Nature. This is particularly supportive of the next practice, Indoor Nature Break. Experiment with different Nature soundscapes, and observe how your body, mind, and emotions respond. A soundscape that is calming to me might be like nails on a chalkboard for you. Choose a Nature soundscape that is right for you and have it at the ready.

With the next practice, the Indoor Nature Break, try selecting a soundscape that aligns with the element of Nature you are connecting with. For example, the native habitat of most indoor plants is a rainforest; they have adapted to low light conditions being near the forest floor. For my Indoor Nature Break practice, I use a soundscape recorded in a temperate rainforest. If you are looking at the trees outside your window or sitting with a water feature, think about what sounds would enhance a connection with them.

## Visual

Ideally, your nest would be positioned so you have a view out the window. Even if the view isn't of Nature, you have natural light coming in and hopefully can see the sky. Try incorporating the four elements or plants as part of your nesting spot. To me, a plant represents all the elements in one: water within the plant's cells; earth (soil or rock) that the plant is rooted within; air that the plant exchanges and purifies; and fire, the innate intelligence or spirit of a plant. There are many creative ways to bring the elements in; sit in your nest area and let it speak to you. What appeals to you and works with your space? Perhaps a water feature, a wood carving, a rock, or a candle.

## Touch

Sensory neurons densely populating your skin send your brain a wide array of information. To stimulate this sense indoors, think creatively. For example, sitting by a window or in an atrium allows you to feel the warmth on your skin, or sitting by an open window might allow you to feel the breeze. Perhaps the feel of a smooth rock or soft alpaca fur are soothing and supportive. If you are doing the Indoor Nature Break practice, try loosening an article of clothing and slipping off your shoes. This will also shift the awareness of what you are feeling on your skin and wake up your nervous system.

## Taste

A creative and easy way to stimulate this sense is to take a digestive bitter before practice. Taking a digestive bitter will give you a feeling like you took a nibble from an edible that you foraged from the wild. As a bonus, digestive bitters directly support your digestive system, which many people need. The American diet tends to lack bitters, which are important to a healthy digestive system and has numerous health benefits. There are many digestive bitters on the market, and you can easily make your own. Common herbs for digestive bitters include dandelion root, burdock root, and gentian root.

You can also stimulate this sense and enhance your health by having a cup of warm herbal tea. Enjoying a cup of tea is a practice all of its own and is described in the Cup of Tea Practice in chapter seven.

In summary, invite the following calming sensory experiences into your home or office nest:
1. Smell - essential oils
2. Sound - your pre-selected soundscape
3. Visual - an element from Nature or window view
4. Touch - feel Nature on your skin
5. Taste - digestive bitter or tea

## PRACTICE 13: Indoor Nature Break

Have you ever been frustrated with something not working, and as a last resort, you unplug it, wait, then plug it back in? It's amazing how often this works. Unplugging for a few moments is just what you will be doing with this practice. Even a couple of minutes is enough to press "reset"' on your "operating system."

This is a practice to have in your back pocket at times when the weather, physical limitations, or overbooked schedule get in your way of getting outside.

To get the most out of your Nature Break and for it to be a practice you return to, the setting is important. It takes just a moment to set yourself up for a delightful Indoor Nature Break. Being intentional with this practice pays off with the restoration of your nervous system and cognitive functioning. The previous practice, Nature-Inspired Nest, can support you in creating a Nature sensory experience for your Nature Break.

With this practice, you are inviting Nature to support you in directing your focus to the here and now within the indoor environment. A view out of the window, a candle flame, water moving in a fountain, or a house plant are examples of allies for this practice. In addition, scents and sounds that you bring into this practice can be supportive points of focus.

In this practice, as your attention is directed outward, you will also feel your body being supported by the chair or the floor beneath you. You allow yourself to settle into your body and the present moment.

**A helpful tip for this practice:**
If you have found a Nature soundscape or scent for this practice that is particularly calming or grounding, practice with it over a few sessions. You will begin to associate the specific stimulus (smell, for example) with the desired state, such as relaxation or mental clarity and focus. Over time, you will be amazed at how quickly your body responds to that stimulus and shifts into the present moment or reestablishes centeredness and clarity after turmoil.

## The practice:

**1.** Begin by selecting your spot or nest for this practice. Make sure it feels safe and comfortable so you can experience restoration. If you choose, turn on your soundscape and diffuse or smell your essential oil. If practical, slip off your shoes or loosen any restrictive clothing.

**2.** Set your intention, timer (if using), and settle in your body with the Body Practice (or any practice to feel your body).
- Begin with three intentional breaths to help transition to this practice. Inhale through your nose for a count of four, then slowly exhale through your mouth for a count of eight. (Feel free to change the count, but have your exhale be longer than your inhale). Allow your inhalation and exhalation through your nose to be soft and easy for the duration of the practice.
- If you feel settled, continue to the next step, but continue to notice your breath through this practice; it is an anchor to the present moment.

**3.** Now direct your focus to your senses, one by one—sound, touch, scent, visual. Feel the aliveness of your body at the same time that you are directing your focus outward toward your present-moment allies.

**4.** If you notice that you are starting to think, allow the thoughts to float by without giving them your attention. Allow your senses to bring you back to the present moment and the felt sense of your body.

- Allow the experience to unfold without effort—simply be in this moment. You are taking a break.

**5.** Conclude with gratitude for yourself for taking this needed break and for your allies in this practice.

## PRACTICE 14: **Eating with Intention**

Humans' relationship to food is complicated. It can be a means of survival, a pleasurable community experience, or even a way to self-medicate for emotions. Developing a healthy relationship and connection with the plants and animals from which our food comes nourishes our body and spirit and is foundational to wellness. Over time, this practice can support the undoing of unhealthy patterns that we may have established with food.

Eating an apple with intention, for example, can be an absolutely delightful sensory experience. Multiple senses are engaged in this encounter with an apple. Typically, we bite into an apple without thought, and then we are done without any connection with the apple, our senses, or our body. We don't even know if our appetite has been satiated.

With this practice, we slow down time. I was first introduced to the idea of mindful eating through the writings of Thich Nhat Hanh, who described mindfully eating a raisin. Right away, I started leading this practice with young people, and they loved it. With the eating with intention practice, I've added a level of body awareness, noting if you are hungry before you begin eating, how your body responds while you are eating, whether you feel satisfied after you eat, and noticing how your body digested the food you just ate. If you feel bloated soon after, this could be an indication that your body doesn't digest this type of food well.

When you are aware of your body, you know what type of foods it needs, when to eat, and the quantity. When you have body awareness around the food you eat, you can more easily throw out all the "shoulds," trends, and rules around eating. It's about making nourishing choices that work best for your body. Be your own food guide.

For this practice, make a conscious choice as to which meal or snack you will commit to eating in this way, and choose foods that are minimally processed. Throughout this practice, your awareness is on your body and the plant or animal you are eating. If you get distracted during practice, allow your senses to bring you back to the present moment.

### The practice:

**1.** Notice your breath, your feet on the floor, and the chair supporting your body. Lengthen your spine and allow your shoulders to relax. Try the Body Practice (chapter five) to enhance the felt awareness of your body as you eat.
   • Tune into how your body feels right now. Are you hungry, craving something to eat but not hungry, not hungry and eating according to schedule? Please do this in a nonjudgmental, awareness-building way.

**2.** Bring your full attention to what you are about to eat.
   • Can you imagine the landscape in which it grew?
   • Bring to your mind's eye the plant or animal's experience with the natural world of sunny days, rains, and changes in the seasons. It lived its life in direct contact with the earth, receiving nourishment.
   • Take a moment to have gratitude for the plant or animal that has become your source of nourishment.

**3.** Before you take a bite, pause to smell what you are about to eat. Notice your body responding.

**4.** Now take your first bite. What flavors and textures are you noticing? Can you tune into the subtlety of what you are eating?

- As you slowly chew, receive the nutrients and energy this plant or animal gives you as though you are receiving a gift. This is an act of gratitude and prepares your body to receive.
- Slowing down also causes you to relax, thus helping your parasympathetic nervous system be more effective at doing its job, helping you digest.
- Pause and notice shifts in your body as you eat this way. How does this compare to how you normally eat?

**5.** Take your time eating. What you eat will be more satisfying, and you will know when you have had enough.

**6.** How do you feel after you eat? Pause, and bring awareness to your body.

- Do you feel more energized, centered, tired, or bloated?
- Noticing how your body responds to what you eat can give you valuable information about what foods work best for your body.

## PRACTICE 15: Sweet Sipping of Cordials

Simply the name of this practice invites you to slow down, take a seat, and rock for a spell. This sweet practice brings us back into right relationship with enjoying imbibing in moderation as a celebration of life, a way to preserve and receive the medicine of plants, and to share company with others and the plant world.

Many practices in this book can be done every day with great benefit. However, this is an every-now-and-again practice. If your relationship with alcohol has been an unhealthy one, I recommend skipping this practice altogether. The Cup of Tea practice in chapter seven is completely interchangeable with this one.

Enjoy this practice by the fire, looking out the window, or as a shared experience. I have included this as an indoor practice but consider taking it out to your porch, rooftop, or backyard. If you have a cordial glass, that's delightful, but a shot glass or small jelly jar work as well.

The key to the practice is intentionally creating an experience from start to finish. What are you sipping out of, where are you sipping, and who are you sipping with? To experience the plant fully, you might want to initially do this practice alone, so you have your full attention on the plant and its medicine.

This practice is connected with the Crafting Cordial Practice in the next chapter. With this practice, you are delighting in the fruits of your labor. If you grew and harvested the flowers or leaves for making this cordial, you've had a relational experience from beginning to end. The flower or leaves you harvested over a month ago might be just the medicine you need now. Cordial crafting is the ultimate slow medicine, and slow sipping is just the right way to take your medicine.

### The practice:

**1.** Once you take your seat, pause and settle in. Feel held by the chair and try the Body Practice to help you settle in even more.

**2.** Lift your glass, observe the color, and smell the sweetness of the cordial. Give gratitude to the plant and their medicine. As you do this, bring the plant into your mind's eye and connect with them from your heart.

**3.** As you take your first sip, savor it. Hold it in your mouth for a moment before swallowing. What subtle flavors do you detect? Notice how your body responds as you take in the sweetness of this cordial.

**4.** Sip slowly and pause a lot. Allow the experience to unfold and just be in the moment.

## PRACTICE 16: **Elemental Embodiment**

As babes, we spoke the language of the natural world, the language of the subtle. The subtle messages from the wind, sun, water, and earth that landed on our skin or were felt in our hearts were preverbal. This language has been whispered since the beginning of time—before human language.

Elemental wisdom is woven within the fabric of our being: soma, emotions, mind, and spirit. Minerals of the earth knitted our bones together, water began flowing through us in utero, air filled our lungs as we emerged from the womb, and fire lit up our passion for exploring a new world. When you reclaim this elemental wisdom within your body, you come home to yourself and align your nervous system and inner landscape to what is true.

With this practice, you call upon the wisdom of the four directions and elements. As an embodiment practice, you are invited to feel the sensations of your body, take up space within your body, and notice subtle shifts that arise with each direction and element. This practice supports you in orienting back to your body, reclaiming your true nature, and reminds you that you are intrinsically woven into the tapestry of all creation.

For audio recordings, visit naturesoma.com/reset.

### The practice:

Before you begin, you've got to know where you are. Whether inside or outside, where does the sun rise, move across the sky, and then set? If it is morning, you can look for the rising sun or use a compass app on your phone to determine the directions. Orienting to where you are within a landscape is both honoring to the land you stand on and brings greater awareness to the moment.

## EAST—AIR/WIND—SPRING

Begin by facing East. East is the land of the new day sun—it represents new beginnings, possibilities, and a fresh start. It is these qualities that we invite within ourselves. East is also connected with the element of air and wind. With each breath, you invite openness and spaciousness, welcoming the newness and potential of this moment—like the first flower of spring.

The movement of this practice involves making fluid, spiraling motions with your arms and upper body, reminiscent of flowing wind. You begin below your hips or first chakra and then spiral your arms all the way to the crown of your head. You can follow the path of your chakras or freestyle. Once you have made your way to your crown, you will spiral back down.

**1.** Facing East, with feet shoulder-width apart, find length in your spine as your shoulders roll back and settle down over your hips. Step your right foot forward and place your left hand, with all fingertips touching each other like a closed clam, in the small of your back behind your belly button.

**2.** Begin by reaching your right arm towards the outside of your body, taking a full breath in through your nose as you reach out and sweep your arm across the front of your body until it reaches the other side. Imagine you are gathering qi (life force energy) and nourishing your body with it. As your hand crosses your body, you slowly exhale, releasing all your breath through your nose as your arm extends to an open position. You will pause with your arm extended until you fully release the breath before you inhale and spiral your arms again.

**3.** You will continue this movement until you reach the crown of your head, spiral towards the heavens, and then spiral down on the same path you ascended.

**4.** Return to the starting position of feet shoulder-width apart. Now step your left foot forward and place your right hand in the small of your back. Repeat previous movement.

**5.** Once complete, pause, and notice any shifts in your body. Feel the quality of openness and spaciousness within you. End with hands to heart center, giving gratitude to the East, the element of Air, and new beginnings and possibilities that each moment holds. Now take a quarter turn to the South.

## SOUTH—FIRE—SUMMER

Throughout the day, the sun makes its journey across the southern sky. We orient our garden beds and solar panels to the south in order to capture the sun's energy for growth and creation. As we face south, we take a moment to pause and tend to sacred fires within. We invite the creative energy, vitality, and passion of South's fire to stoke our inner fire.

You will practice two movements as you face the South. The first movement is with the intention of receiving and tending to your heart fire, before the second movement of giving.

### Receiving

**1.** With feet shoulder-width apart, find length in your spine as your shoulders roll back and settle down over your hips. Place your hands on your heart. Feel the sensation in the center, front, and back of your heart.

**2.** As you inhale through your nose, extend your arms out as though you are about to give someone an embrace, and sweep your arms forward as though you are receiving something precious, then bring your arms back, fingers meeting at your heart. As your hands return to your heart, exhale. Let your hands settle here for a moment and feel your heart area.

**3.** What do you notice—can you soften and open your heart to receive more? What do you need to receive from this direction that would stoke your heart fire—love, energy, passion, creativity? Invite this in and be nourished by it. You give so much throughout your day; now it is time to intentionally receive.

Continue this fluid motion of receiving and nourishing until you feel complete or for at least nine cycles.

## Giving

This powerhouse move reframes our notion of giving at a somatic and spiritual level. Through this movement, we remember that we are conduits of divine grace, abundance, and love, with energy flowing through us. This is an effortless and potent way to give and share your gifts with the world.

With this movement, play with the imaginal and energetic. Begin by feeling and giving attention to the area behind your heart. With this movement, you are breathing through the back of your heart, receiving life force energy (love-consciousness, whatever language best serves you), and allow it to flow through your heart outward into the world. In a sense, you are allowing yourself to be breathed by All That Is.

As you open and receive the flow of this energy through the back of your heart, it mixes with your heart fire and creates alchemy with your divine spark and the light of all creation. This flow of energy moving through you is a potent gift to the world, offered from a place of abundance and effortlessness. It is also healing for your heart to be a conduit of grace and loving-kindness.

**1.** The movement begins with your hands cupped at your heart center, inhaling through your nose and inviting life-force energy to flow into the back of your heart. Then, as you exhale through your nose, you open your arms outward as an offering of this abundance of love, grace, and goodness as it flows through you. In this fluid motion of giving, you pause as your arms spread wide, leaning backward with your heart forward, trusting that the universe has your back.

**2.** Repeat this movement until you feel complete, or at least nine times. Pause, and notice the area around your heart.

What has shifted, and what sensations do you feel around your heart and throughout your body?

**3.** Give gratitude to the South, the growth and abundance of summer, the sacred fire within, and sacred fires everywhere. Now take a quarter turn to the West.

## WEST—WATER—FALL

At this point in our practice, we have moved through the East, breathing life into new beginnings and possibilities. With the sun's fire in the southern sky, we have stoked our heart's fire and danced with giving and receiving. Now we find ourselves in the West, connected with the season of fall, and we move from the energy of creativity and growth to one of honoring and gratitude for the harvest. You have done enough, and you are enough. It is time to slow down, settle in, and be.

The direction of West is connected with the element of water, and it is with this medicine that you reclaim flow to your body, mind, and spirit. You are reminded to enter into the flow of life—effortlessly flowing with All That Is.

**1.** Begin with your arms by your side, your feet shoulder-width apart, your spine long, and roll your shoulders down and back. The movement of the West is reminiscent of waves in the ocean. As you inhale through your nose, gently allow your arms to float up to waist height as you slightly rise on your toes. This movement is slow and graceful as your arms effortlessly rise up and then lower back down—as if the ocean is floating them. Your hands are soft and as fluid as your arms. As you exhale, allow your arms to flow softly down by your side, and your heels to touch the ground.

**2.** On your next inhalation, allow your arms to float slightly higher, then gently float down by your side on the exhale. Continue this movement, raising your arms higher with each breath until they reach overhead, the biggest wave.

**3.** Now continue moving in waves, but essentially in reverse, allowing your waves to become smaller and smaller until the last one is at waist height again.

**4.** Pause and feel the fluidity of your body, your "enoughness," gratitude for this moment, and gratitude to the West and the sacred waters within and all around. Now take a quarter turn to the North.

## NORTH—EARTH—WINTER

North holds the wisdom of winter and the wisdom of the earth—both offering the gift and lessons of rest and restoration. We have made our way through the wheel of life and settled into the wisdom of our bodies. Everything requires rest and stillness; from this, new life can emerge with vitality and potency.

Facing North, we allow the clay of our bodies to settle into the clay of the earth as her energies rise up to meet us. The minerals that knit together our bones and flow through our blood are the same as those in the "body" of the earth. We pause as we connect with the mother of all.

When I lead this movement with children, I call this a mama earth bath.

**1.** Begin by imagining that you have etheric fingers that extend past your physical ones. Then, with a fluid motion, fold at the hips, allowing your arms to float down, and as you inhale, imagine that you are reaching into the earth, receiving her energy and allowing it to flow through your feet, legs, trunk, and out the crown of your head. Your hands move upward as you receive the "groundedness," stability, and sweetness of the earth's energy flowing through your body. It's as if your hands are helping to guide the flow of energy and supporting you with felt awareness of your body.

**2.** As you exhale, allow your arms, which at this point are extended over your head, to gently float down your side body.

With this downward motion, you can intend to clear the energy around you. As your arms float down, past your hips, begin to fold over as your arms make their way back to the ground for another round of movement with your inhalation.

**3.** Continue until you feel complete or for at least nine cycles. With your last exhalation, bring your hands to heart center and give gratitude for the North, the earth beneath your feet, her wisdom knitted into the fabric of your being, and for coming home to yourself. Pause here, notice what has shifted in your body, and allow yourself to rest and be still.

## CLOSING & CONNECTION

We end this practice with a movement that reminds us of our inherent connection to all the biotic (living) and abiotic (non-living), the seen and unseen. We pluck the energetic strings that weave us into the tapestry of creation as a reminder of what is true and our true home.

**1.** With feet shoulder-width apart, spine long, arms by your side, and slightly leaning backward with heart forward—inhale as you sweep your arms out to the side with your palms face up. As your arms reach above your head, begin to exhale, and imagine you are welcoming and inviting golden threads of light through the crown of your head and feel these threads flow through your head, trunk, legs, and back into the earth. Your hands will softly follow that path of these threads down your core, in front of your body.

**2.** Continue this movement until you feel complete, or for at least nine cycles—end with bringing your hands to the heart center. Pause and notice what has shifted within your body, mind, and spirit. Offer gratitude to all that is and feel yourself resting as you find yourself being completely supported by the threads that connect you with all of creation.

# neighborhood practices

**17.** Connected Walking  **18.** Patio or Backyard Gardening
**19.** Cordial Making  **20.** Exercise Upleveled

The practices in this chapter are a creative way to bloom right where you are planted. They take activities that you are already doing and turn them into much-needed restorative experiences right outside your door. Perhaps you've never grown a kitchen garden but have always wanted to—now is a great time to start! Gardening can be both productive and provide cognitive and emotional restoration. It might become your favorite way to get your daily dose of Nature.

For those of us feeling squeezed for time, some of these neighborhood practices fit in seamlessly. Try Connected Walking when headed to a meeting—even five minutes of this practice can clear your mind and refocus you on the task ahead. The Exercise Upleveled practice meets your need to nourish with both movement and Nature connection. You are getting two benefits in one activity. This type of nourishment-stacking applies to gardening as well. Movement + Nature + Growing Nourishing Food = Power Packed Nature Practice.

My hope is that the practices within this chapter will inspire you to create Nature practices out of activities outdoors that you are already doing. Getting your daily dose of Nature can combine fun, restoration, and productivity all in one activity.

## PRACTICE 17: Connected Walking

You might be saying, "I already walk outside in my neighborhood or around my office; how is this a practice?" My response is, do you feel restored afterward? That is the difference. A subtle shift in how you walk turns an everyday activity into a moment of restoration.

With this short practice, you completely unplug from all devices. Talking on the phone, listening to music, pings of notifications going off, or listening to a podcast—things many of us do while walking, can create a veil of distraction. We are here, but not fully here—devices create a subtle or not-so-subtle separation from the awareness of our body and the trees, plants, wind, and animals in our neighborhood.

In this practice, you are aware of your body as you walk, and you invite the states of openness and fluidity or ease to settle within you as you connect with the natural world around you. For example, a moment with a dandelion growing through a crack in the sidewalk can offer you a reminder of your own inner resilience—a sweet moment of connection.

Here's an example of how I use this in my own life: When going to a meeting, I have a choice of where my attention is during the ten-minute walk. I can look at my phone, I can dwell in my thoughts, or I can be fully in the moment. If I walk with awareness, noticing my feet making contact with the earth, noticing my breath, as well as connecting with the plants and trees that I pass, I arrive at my meeting in a totally different state than when I started walking. I am grounded, have more clarity, and am more open to possibilities. I bring all these qualities into my meeting as a result of choosing awareness and connection as I walk.

**The practice:**

**1.** Set your intention and settle in your body with the Body Practice (or any practice to feel your body). Allow your inhalation and exhalation through your nose to be soft and easy for the duration of the practice.

**2.** As you walk, notice your feet touching the ground. Notice your breath, lengthen your spine and drop your shoulders. Allow yourself to walk with fluidity—you are feeling your body as you walk, intending to soften areas that feel tense and moving with ease. Let thoughts gently go as they arise.

**3.** Bring your attention to your senses. Notice the wind and sun on your skin, smells, sounds, and allow your gaze to rest and be with one being or element from the natural world at a time. This is a moment of acknowledgment and connection.
  • If you live in an urban area and the city sounds are too distracting, try listening to a soundscape as you walk if this seems supportive. Construction or city noises can also be an opportunity to practice selective listening or intentionally directing your focus. Can you allow human-made sounds to fade to the background and bring forward the sound of birds, for example?

**4.** As you walk and connect with your surroundings through your gaze, bring your felt awareness to the area around your heart. See if you can feel states such as openness, gratitude, or loving-kindness rise within you. (see Heart Practice in chapter five). Connect with the Nature surrounding you— through your heart.

**5.** End your walk with gratitude for this time you carved out for yourself and the connections you made.

PRACTICE 18: **Patio/Backyard Garden Cultivation**

Tending to or co-creating with the natural world is a delightful spiritual practice. As one who can be a busy bee, gardening is a practice that invites me to slow down, settle within the clay of my body as I touch the earth, and sweetly connect with the natural world.

Gardening is a creative and experimental process that connects us with the rhythms and cycles of the natural world and puts us in a direct relationship with plants, pollinators, the changing seasons, and the microbial world. Many people still sow seeds, tend to plants, and harvest by the moon's cycles. We can enter back into this relationship right in our backyards and patios and receive the gifts of nourishing our bodies and the therapeutic benefits of restoration to our nervous systems and spirits.

When in the garden, we enter the sweet relationship of tending to, listening deeply, and flowing with the next right thing. With any type of gardening, I always recommend growing what you love—whether it's flowers, herbs, fruit trees, berry bushes, vegetables, or a mix of all of it.

A garden is a very intimate way of relating with the natural world because you're co-creating. You help create a vibrant soil population of diverse microbes and invertebrates, which in turn helps to nurture healthy, vibrant plants. You have the honor of tending to the soil and the plants, which has the added benefit of supporting pollinators, wildlife, and nourishing food and medicine for you. If you are interested in learning more about collaborating with Nature to cultivate plants, you will find biodynamic farming, permaculture, and the Findhorn Society fascinating.

What makes this a practice vs. gardening? Your intention and awareness. There might be times when you need to tend to a few things quickly. This is great; however, it's different than practice. It becomes a practice when you have intentionally set this time apart for you to settle into your body, observe the subtle, "listen" to your garden, and allow your garden work to "unfold." It could actually take the same amount of time, but the intention is very different. You are collaborating with your garden and learning from the garden about what it needs rather than doing something to it. This is how one truly becomes a master gardener or co-creator.

When gardening is a practice, you might have an objective in mind, such as, "I want to sow beet seeds." However, hold this lightly, as well as how you think you are going to do it. As you tune into your garden, you might realize that the beets would actually be best planted somewhere else than your original plan. How you go about preparing the soil might also change as you slow down and listen. As you sow the seeds, you do this with tenderness and respect and bless them as they germinate and grow.

In general, with gardening, as with many things, we put forth more effort than we need to. This practice helps us to get into a slower state of mind. If we're moving very quickly about our garden, we're going to do things that don't need to be done. For example, some weeds can be beneficial! When you go slowly, you can notice the actual needs of the ecosystem.

Please see Appendix A for helpful tips on getting your backyard or patio garden started. One of the easiest ways to get started is by growing perennial herbs. Below is a chart with easy-to-grow perennials and how they support your body and your backyard ecosystem. Hopefully, this will inspire you to get started! Please note, before taking herbal formulas, consult your health care professional.

Interesting note—when my garden feels untended to, I often find that I'm not tending to myself as well. My garden often reflects the state of my inner landscape. Listen, and much wisdom will be shared with you.

## The practice:

**1.** Settle in your body with the Body Practice (or any practice to feel your body). Allow your inhalation and exhalation through your nose to be soft and easy for the duration of the practice.

**2.** Feel your feet connecting to the earth and look around your garden, not with the quality of an inspection, but as you would lovingly watch a child playing. What do you notice? What is asking to be tended to? What is asking to be left alone? Before doing anything, observe. And observe some more.

**3.** What feels like the most honoring way to start tending to your garden? Start there and notice what unfolds.

**4.** If you notice that your mind is elsewhere, gently invite it back to the garden.

**5.** When you are complete with your practice, end with intention. Slowly tend to the tools you used and give gratitude to this garden community that you are part of and co-creating with.

### Easy-to-Grow Perennials That Support You and Ecosystems

| HERB/PLANT | ECOSYSTEM FUNCTION | MEDICINAL SUPPORT | PART AND FORM USED | PLANT PREFERENCES |
|---|---|---|---|---|
| **elderberry** <br> *Sambucus canadensis* | wildlife habitat; supports pollinators | immune system support, colds, flu, upper respiratory infections | ripe berries: tea, tincture, syrup | full sun / partial shade; moderate water; well-drained soil |
| **echinacea** <br> *Echinacea purpurea, Echinacea angustifolia* | nectar source for butterflies and supports other pollinators | immune system booster | root and leaves: tincture or tea | full sun; low water |
| **lavender** <br> *Lavandula angustifolia* | supports honeybees and other pollinators | calms nervous system, heals burns, antiseptic | flowers: tea, tincture, skin salve | full sun; low water; well-drained sandy soil |

# Easy-to-Grow Perennials That Support You and Ecosystems

| HERB/PLANT | ECOSYSTEM FUNCTION | MEDICINAL SUPPORT | PART AND FORM USED | PLANT PREFERENCES |
|---|---|---|---|---|
| **lemon balm**<br>Melissa officinalis | supports honeybees and other pollinators | antiviral for herpes, shingles, and colds; calms nervous digestion | leaves: tea, tincture | full sun / partial shade; well-drained soil; spreads rapidly-best in contained area. |
| **motherwort**<br>Mentha piperita | supports honeybees and other pollinators | calms heart palpitations or irregular heartbeat; nervous system tonic: soother if feeling frazzled, overwhelmed, anxiety and depression | flowering parts and leaves: tincture and tea (bitter) | full sun / partial shade; low to moderate water |
| **peppermint**<br>Sambucus canadensis | nectar for butterflies and supports other pollinators | digestive aid - eases nausea and stomach cramps | leaves: tea | full sun / partial shade / shade; spreads rapidly-best in contained area |
| **oregano**<br>Origanum vulgare | supports beneficial insects, bees, and pollinators | winter immune support; digestive support | leaves: culinary, tincture, tea | full sun / partial shade; well-drained soil |
| **rosemary**<br>Rosmarinus officinalis | supports honeybees and other pollinators | antioxidant; winter immune support; digestive support; circulatory support | leaves: culinary, tincture, tea | full sun; well-drained soil |
| **thyme**<br>Thymus vulgaris, Thymus serpyllum | supports honeybees and other pollinators | winter immune support; digestive support; strong antibacterial and antiseptic | leaves: culinary, tincture, tea | full sun / partial shade; well-drained soil |
| **yarrow**<br>Achillea millefolium | supports butterflies and other pollinators; attracts beneficial insects such as ladybugs and predatory wasps | antimicrobial; anti-inflammatory; amazing for stings of all types; stops drainage of all kinds | flowering parts and leaves: tincture, skin salve, powdered for wounds, tea (bitter) | full sun / partial shade; low to moderate water; well-drained soil |

## PRACTICE 19: **Crafting Cordials**

Crafting medicinal cordials can be an adventure, a throwback to slower times, a way to nourish the body and soul, and a sweet way to gather with friends. With this practice, you forage or harvest from your garden medicinal flowers or leaves of the season. I like to describe the sweetness and vitality of cordials as the "nectar of the gods," which lifts the spirit (if used in moderation).

Gathering plants for cordials is a practice that cultivates and heightens our awareness of what is happening in the natural world. For example, some flowers for medicine or cordial making have a brief window for harvest, and then the opportunity is gone. This requires us to be on the lookout each season for that sweet plant medicine we want to bring into our lives.

If you live in the city, you can still grow, harvest, and make your own cordials. Lemon balm easily grows in abundance in a south-facing window. Voila—you can make your own homegrown, homemade cordial in the middle of New York City!

Know that cordials are alcoholic beverages, so they are not for everyone. Any plant that you use for cordial making can also make the most delightful cup of tea.

This crafting practice begins with harvesting and then cordial making. With each of these steps, the secret ingredient is presence and intention. The final practice is actually in chapter nine, the Sweet Sipping of Cordials. Medicinal flowers that make lovely cordials include violets, elderberry, lavender, dandelion, honeysuckle, rose, and goldenrod. The leaves of lemon balm and peppermint also make delightful cordials.

### The HARVESTING practice:

The preparation for this practice is to stop and smell the roses (or violets or dandelions). In other words, be on the lookout for flowers in their prime: recently opened, fresh-looking, with no petals falling off. If you are foraging (see Foraging, practice 22), only harvest if there is an abundance—harvest just what you need, leaving plenty for pollinators and plant reproduction. In addition, please make sure you have a 100% identification of the flowers/leaves you are gathering. Some plants can be poisonous and have look-a-likes.

Begin the practice of harvesting by settling into your body and the moment with The Body Practice. Feeling your feet on the ground, settling into your hips by feeling yourself occupy the space within, and paying attention to your rhythmic breathing. While harvesting, try to maintain this level of awareness in your body. Next, bring your attention to the plants you are harvesting. Take them in with all your senses. Notice where they are living and with whom they live (birds, insects, and others in the plant community).

With gratitude, begin to harvest. With each flower picked, feel an inner thank you towards the plant, fully receiving the gifts of the moment and the medicine from the plant. This in itself is a heart-opening practice.

### The CORDIAL-MAKING practice:

**1.** After gathering your herbs, put them into a mason jar (pint or quart, depending on how much you have). You don't want to pack them in but fill it well. You can chop them up, but I love to leave the flower whole. For me, part of the experience is enjoying looking at them in the jar as I regularly shake them.

**2.** Fill the jar with vodka. Use the highest quality that makes sense for you.

**3.** Cap and label your jar with the plant name and date harvested. I like to cover the bottom of the mason jar lid with parchment paper to prevent any corrosion of the lid.

**4.** Place in a dark space (a cabinet is great) and shake a few times each week. Each time you go to shake it, pause and connect with the herbs you harvested. Delight in them, and their medicine will be even sweeter.

**5.** In four-six weeks, it will be ready to strain. You do this by placing cheesecloth in a strainer, enough to where it lays over the side of the strainer. You should be able to pull the sides up and give the herbs a good squeeze to make sure you have extracted all the medicine from the plants.

**6.** Now you have a medicinal tincture. You could stop here and use it as a tincture or continue and add simple syrup to create the cordial.

### Making a simple syrup:

**1.** Put one cup of sugar and one cup of water into a saucepan. You may adjust this to how much tincture/infused vodka you have. Just keep the 1:1 ratio the same.

**2.** On medium heat, warm and stir until sugar has dissolved into the water.

**3.** Let the simple syrup cool.

### Final step:

Mix the herb-infused vodka with the simple syrup. Many people use a 2:1 ratio; however, experiment with the level of sweetness that you prefer. Store your cordial in a cool, dark location and enjoy within a year of making (Practice 15: Sweet Sipping of Cordials).

## PRACTICE 20: **Exercise Upleveled**

Some athletes may not understand why they would need these practices because they're outside all the time. I get it. I was a marathon runner. When I was running, I felt really good and really clear. But it was always short-lived. When I was hitting those high miles, I was unaware that I was trying to feel my body and a sense of aliveness that often eluded me. At times it was a compulsion, as I was going after the dopamine hit and a sense of being grounded.

For most of those miles, I was a passerby or spectator within the landscape. I didn't see myself as part of it. I might have noticed a lovely flower, but that was where the experience stopped— with a noticing. I received the benefits of exercise but not the long-term restoration that connecting with where I was could have gifted me, which my nervous system desperately needed.

With this practice, as with all other Nature Reset Practices, you settle into your body as you connect with the Natural world around you. You might choose to do this practice for the first ten minutes of your workout. Or at the end when you stretch your body. Adding the element of Nature to your workout will add an extra boost to your emotional and mental well-being. Local parks, greenways, neighborhood sidewalks, and backyards are great locations for this practice.

If you tend to go to a gym, check out these outdoor alternatives to popular gym activities.

- Treadmill: walk, jog, run, sprint outside

- Stairmaster: find stairs outside or a hill (it is helpful to have cleats for this)

- Stationary bike: greenways are popping up in cities around the country, and they are great places to ride your bike

- <u>Weightlighting:</u> free weights and kettlebells can easily move outdoors for a backyard workout
- <u>Swimming pool:</u> open water swimming with a group
- <u>Find these classes outside or do it yourself:</u> yoga, tai chi, Qigong

If you have physical limitations or cannot leave your house, try to position your workout equipment to face a window.

## The practice:

**1.** Set your intention and settle in your body with the Body Practice (or any practice to feel your body). Remember to unplug from your devices while you are committed to this practice.

**2.** As you feel your feet connecting with the earth, feel the solidness and aliveness of your legs, core, and arms. Try to keep this level of body awareness as you exercise or stretch.

**3.** While you are moving your body within this landscape, notice what has changed since the last time you were there. Be curious. Allow the search for the novelty to support you with resting your attention in the present moment.

**4.** Seek beauty in the subtle within your neighborhood; you might be pleasantly surprised! What inspires gratitude? Can you feel a connection with the plant community or elements of nature that catch your eye?

**5.** As you exercise, continue to return your focus to your body, breath, and your senses. With exercise, our mind can sometimes drift elsewhere, especially if the workout gets hard.

**6.** When you are complete, take a moment to give gratitude for this time of strengthening your body, mind, and spirit as well as the natural world that you connected with.

You can also apply this same practice to any adventure you undertake. With adventure, there is an element (or perceived element) of risk and novelty. Your awareness is heightened, and you feel more alive than in your regular routine. Your senses become sharper, and your attention is more focused on the present moment. Adventure is food for the soul.

While having an outdoor adventure, the above practice will enhance your experience even more. Choose a specific and safe time on your adventure to bring in this level of awareness. As you practice, intentionally open your heart to the experience of connecting with the natural world around you while maintaining awareness of all that you are sensing within your body.

Keep reading—the next chapter is all about Nature connection adventures.

THE NATURE RESET

........................................................................................................

........................................................................................................

........................................................................................................

........................................................................................................

........................................................................................................

........................................................................................................

........................................................................................................

........................................................................................................

........................................................................................................

........................................................................................................

........................................................................................................

........................................................................................................

........................................................................................................

........................................................................................................

 FIELD NOTES

CHAPTER 11

# nature adventures

21. Forest Bathing  22. Foraging
23. Retreating and Adventures in Nature  24. Guiding Kids in Nature

Sometimes, things just need to simmer—like a delicious hearty stew, giving the flavors time to dance together and infuse. We need time to "simmer" in the natural world—to be infused and nourished by its stillness, awe-inspiring complexity, truth-sharing, and beauty. This takes time—but the end results are deep restoration, the awakening of parts that have fallen asleep, and the reclamation of your inner landscape.

Practices in this chapter ask for you to linger longer in the natural world, to slow down time, deeply unfurl, and infuse yourself with the gifts of the landscape around you. The necessity of carving out time for longer practices in Nature occurred to me while backpacking in Maine on the Appalachian Trail with my family. When I started this two-month summer adventure, I felt like I normally do—with a little apprehension about starting, but the excitement overshadowed my nervousness. I'd be lying if I didn't say I wasn't a little extra nervous about starting this adventure with my eight and eleven-year-old, but we had prepared well as a family, and I knew we could do it.

This backpacking trip also coincided with a time when I was working on developing greater body awareness—to really feel what I was feeling—which is a foundational practice of this book. I had taken numerous long-distance backpacking trips without such awareness. Once in the woods, I could sense a low-level "buzziness" in my body; it was like static that I hadn't noticed before. It felt really uncomfortable and out of place. After two days, the static was gone, and I felt more like myself than I had in a long time. I felt clear and deeply settled. I was not aware of the buzziness of my nervous system that I had become accustomed to until I experienced the extended time of contrast in the woods. The baseline I perceived as "normal" wasn't normal after all; I had just adapted.

Perhaps while on vacation or extended periods of being unplugged you, too, have experienced a reset to your nervous system and the sweet awakening of forgotten parts of yourself. This is the "why" behind the extended practices in this chapter. I recommend an extended practice once a month in addition to your daily Nature Reset practice to deeply support your nervous system and overall well-being.

## PRACTICE 21: Forest Bathing

Forest bathing is like spring cleaning; Nature supports us in clearing out the internal clutter.

I'd like to share my first experience with forest bathing (although unnamed) as a vibrant illustration of this powerful practice. As a fledgling researcher and newbie to the rainforest of Panama, my first few encounters with this landscape were as if I had blinders on. I heard amazing stories from the locals of all that resided within the canopy and forest floor, but I didn't see or experience any of it. My speedy pace of hiking, setting up malaise traps for parasitic wasp research, and looking out for snakes, kept the rainforest's treasures hidden.

Fortunately, a Panamanian elder offered to help me see, and I gratefully took him up on his offer. The first thing he taught me was how to slow down.

During those two hours, we might have exchanged ten words. We communicated with body language and our eyes. His love of the forest emanated through him. He demonstrated how to move through the rainforest slowly, with intention and curiosity. A new world was revealed to me. I could now see the anteater, agouti, coati, and tapir that had been there all along. After overflowing with gratitude to the elder who had helped me have eyes to see, a calm settled over me that remained for days.

I had not heard of forest bathing at the time, but this was my introduction to this life-changing practice. The Panamanian elder and his ancestors delighted in, or "soaked in," the wonders of the rainforest long before the term forest bathing existed.

The art and science of forest bathing, or Shinrin Yoku, loosely translates into "soaking in the forest atmosphere." It's the practice of immersing yourself in a natural setting (not just a forest), wherein you engage all your senses with curiosity and openness. Our everyday practices of Nature connection enhance our forest bathing experience because we have already cultivated inner stillness, the ability to fully experience the natural world through our senses, and connecting with the natural world from the place of the heart.

Forest bathing is different from a hike.

There is no destination. We move slowly, stop, delight, and take everything in through our multitude of senses, just as the Panamanian elder taught me.

This well-researched and therapeutic practice emerged in the 1980s from the Forestry Agency in Japan to encourage individuals to enjoy the forests in order to improve health and well-being. In the 1990s Japan's researchers began to quantify this experience, leading to the development of the concept of Forest Medicine. At this point, the therapeutic practice of forest bathing began to spread across the globe.

Researchers have found forest bathing to decrease stress and anxiety, elevate mood, reduce blood pressure, improve sleep and creativity, and increase immune system function. However, I believe one of the most important aspects of forest bathing is to reconnect back to the natural world and experience the inner peace, contentment, and clarity that resides within us.

## How long?

The human-made, time-bound world stops with a forest bathing practice as you step into timeless presence.

Traditional forest bathing is typically a minimum of two hours. This is not a hike, it is much slower, and there is no destination. Think more like a quarter-mile wander with a few rest stops than a 5-mile hike.

The spaciousness of time that we create around forest bathing allows us to experience more than what we initially perceive at a surface level of awareness. This revelation of the "hidden" was exactly what I experienced in the rainforest when taught by the elder.

For many of us, it has been a while since we've unplugged for such a long period of time. At first, there is a relief, but it can begin to feel a little uncomfortable without the constant inputs we've become habituated to. You have created space to be fully present and aware, so emotions and tension might surface that you didn't even realize were there because of all your typical daily distractions.

This is part of clearing the internal clutter. As your mind declutters, you may find yourself chasing thoughts. Allow things to arise, feeling what comes up, but without mentally attaching to a story. Staying connected with your body and Nature will support the static to settle into peace and clarity.

Decide how long you will be Forest Bathing and commit to that time. Set a timer—a gift to yourself to release tracking time, so you can genuinely enter into timelessness.

## Support or Solo?

Forest bathing can be led by someone who helps you stay present and gives you invitations to settle in more deeply to the experience, or it can be on your own. If you are going out alone, tell someone where you are going and when you expect to return. Dress comfortably, prepare for the weather, and bring water and perhaps a snack. If you plan to end your experience with tea, bring a thermos of hot water. Phones help in an emergency, but even a little ping from a notification can pull your attention from the present moment. Bring your phone but silence it.

## Where?

Forest bathing as a practice and the research supporting its benefits emerged from the evergreen forests of Japan. However, any natural setting works—a forest, estuary, beach, lake, or meadow. Many beautiful parks and botanical gardens also work well for this practice. You must feel safe where you are going so you can let your guard down, relax, and engage fully. Having a guide or partner helps if you don't feel safe or relaxed being out on your own.

You might have minimal experience being out in Nature and are nervous about hazards. Take time to learn about where you are going. The beauty of focusing on what is right in front of you and moving slowly is that many hazards can be avoided. For example, the snake in the path is no longer startling because you move with awareness and curiosity. Now you can admire it from a distance with amazement and not fear. Potential hazards are thwarted, and a new opportunity to connect emerges.

## Intention is everything

Intention, attention, and gratitude support us in connecting deeply with ourselves and the natural world—this is sacred alchemy for healing. While practicing, you maintain an awareness of your internal landscape (feeling your body), the sensory information you receive, and a sense of openness and curiosity.

As you walk about, seek beauty in the unusual, subtle, and show-stopping. Be on the lookout for something to cause wonder and amazement within you. What invites you to pause and take a seat?

Below is a general outline of forest bathing, or more loosely put—a therapeutic experience in Nature. However, use your intuition, available time, and outdoor resources to sculpt your own experience. Many of the practices in the field guide can be brought into your forest bathing experience. Each is an invitation to connect deeply.

When choosing a location to begin, it might not necessarily be a trailhead. Find a spot that feels like a good transition point. Examples of this are: where the path widens or narrows, where thick vegetation makes a marked passageway, a boulder next to the trail, a patch of flowers, and a creek—each of these transition points or "thresholds" invite you to step into a different way of connecting with yourself and the natural world. As you cross over, you leave behind all you have been carrying, invite the static to settle, and step into unencumbered freedom.

## The broad strokes of forest bathing:

**1.** Settle in your body with the Body Practice (or any practice to feel your body). Allow your inhalation and exhalation through your nose to be soft and easy for the duration of the practice.
- Feel your feet making contact with the earth below you. Invite the stability and "groundedness" of the earth to rise up and meet you as you settle down to meet her.

**2.** If you are not already at the transition point or threshold, you will recognize it more clearly now that you have settled in your body.
- Set your intention for your time with Nature, then cross your threshold.

**3.** Orient yourself to the landscape you find yourself in. It is like setting the needle on a compass. You've oriented to your body; now orient to the land.

Notice the information coming through your senses:
- What are you feeling on your skin—the wind, sun, cold?
- What sounds do you begin to notice?
- Are there any scents you can discern?
- Notice the various colors and patterns around you.
- Take a breath through your mouth and get a subtle taste.
- How does being in the presence of a diversity of life and Nature elements make you feel? How is your body beginning to respond?

**4.** Throughout this practice, use your intention, your senses, the felt sense of your body, your connection to the earth, and your breath to bring you back to the present moment. If you get distracted by thoughts, be gentle with yourself, and allow your senses to guide you back to the moment.

**5.** You can't get this practice wrong as long as you keep coming back to the present moment, noticing what catches your attention or how you are feeling. Suspend judgment and allow yourself to be guided by your heart and intuition.

- You might see a spot you would like to sit at for a while. That is the next right step to take. Sit there until you feel called to move to a new spot.
- You might want to remove your shoes and put your feet in the water or bare earth. This is your next right step.
- You might want to close your eyes and listen to the sounds - birds, the wind in the trees. This is your next right step.

**6.** At this point, there are many ways to engage with the natural world around you. Many of the practices in chapters six through eight can serve as ways to deepen your forest bathing experience.

- A super sweet practice that I recommend is allowing yourself to be "seen" by a tree, water, or wind. Imagine that they recognize your presence, truly seeing you. What does that feel like? This is a very powerful practice. Depths are revealed the more you connect in this way.
- Try creating your own ways to connect with Nature; the only limits are your imagination.

**7.** When your forest bathing is complete, simmer in gratitude. Feel it in your body and radiate that gratitude out to the landscape.

- Often, a forest bathing experience ends with a cup of tea made with foraged plants or tea you brought. This is a lovely practice to help you transition from your Nature experience.

After a forest bathing experience, it can be quite supportive for the rest of the day to be slower and have less external stimulus than usual. This allows you to soak in the energy of the experience longer before moving on to everyday obligations.

## PRACTICE 22: **Foraging**

Nature offers us an abundance of food and medicine, often right outside the back door. Wild food has more trace minerals and nutrients than most cultivated food purchased in the grocery store. As a bonus, we experience a release of dopamine, a neurotransmitter that contributes to feeling pleasure and satisfaction, when we harvest food. Researchers have hypothesized that this response has evolved over 200,000 years of hunting and gathering. You can imagine the excitement of finding a patch of wild berries; and the biochemical response to finding such a treasure. Many people experience this same pleasure from shopping.

With foraging, we receive the mental and emotional restorative benefit of being outside, the dopamine release of the harvest, and the nourishment of trace minerals and herbal medicine that supports our physical and emotional well-being.

Often, whatever plants are leafing out or blooming is just what our body needs at that particular time of year. For example, in the transition from winter to spring, across North America, you will see chickweed making a joyful appearance. Chickweed supports the lymphatic system and cleanses the blood after the cold winter months. Pretty amazing, right? Just what we need at just the right time.

Come spring, my yard will be overflowing with an abundance of food. I don't put any chemicals in my yard, so it is full of a diversity of life among the grass. I have plenty of wild food such as violets, purple dead nettle, and lamb's quarters to make salads, greens for sandwiches, smoothies, and to sauté with other veggies. All of these plants are both food and medicine. In the early spring, my garden plot will be full of wild food (see chart below), and I harvest this before I begin to plant cultivated varieties.

You can begin your experience with wild food by getting to know what is growing outside your back door or local public green space. By being an observer, you will build a relationship with these plants, notice how they change in appearance throughout their growth cycle, and where they tend to grow and thrive. Different parts of plants are best harvested at different times of the growing season; a good foraging field guide provides this information. In addition, see how they are best prepared, as some wild edibles need to be parboiled. (See chart below for basic information on common wild food)

With foraging, you need to be 110% confident with your plant identification before harvesting. Some lookalikes can be poisonous, but if you take your time and have multiple resources to reference, you will be amazed by the bounty you can harvest. Once you develop an eye for wild food, you will see an abundance all around you. You will observe Nature and connect with her in a whole new way. However, before you begin harvesting the bounty around you, it's very important to consider location. For example, could it have been exposed to herbicides or pesticides? Runoff from the road? Used as a relief spot for a passing dog? Forage away from roadsides and in areas you are confident have not been sprayed with chemicals.

Foraging becomes a practice when you move with intention and from your heart. Obviously, it is important to bring your mind online for proper identification. Once you're confident of the identification, the search and harvest of wild edibles will come from the heart.

**How to get started:**

1. Start with looking at field guides and reading about foraging. One of my favorites is Edible Wild Plants by John Kallas. He goes into great detail on how these plants change in appearance over a season, how to spot a poisonous lookalike, and includes many recipes. However, there are many other great books

available, as well as websites. With websites be sure to cross-check any information, as inexperienced foragers might be better at blogging than knowing their plants! Foraging is very seasonal and regional, so when seeking information, dial into your specific region of the country and the time of year you are foraging.

What to bring with you:
- Your favorite field guides
- A good quality pruner, hori-hori (Japanese garden knife), kitchen scissors, basket/bucket.

**2.** Settle in your body with the Body Practice (or any practice to feel your body). Allow your inhalation and exhalation through your nose to be soft and easy for the duration of the practice.

**3.** Move slowly and gently on your foraging walkabout. Rest your awareness in your heart; you will actually "see" more.

**4.** Once you have properly identified your plant, it is time to harvest. If you are new to foraging, there has been some mental work to ensure you are 100% accurate in your identification. Now bring your full awareness and presence into the moment as you intentionally harvest. The below steps turn the foraging experience into a therapeutic practice.
- Recenter yourself by feeling your feet on the earth, noticing your breath, and the aliveness of your body. The plant offers their presence; it is a wonderful experience to offer your presence in return.
- Feel the state of gratitude within yourself as you harvest and offer this to the plant.
- When harvesting, only take what you need and be sure to leave at least 2/3 behind of prolific plants to create future offspring. Do not harvest uncommon wild species.

**5.** When you are complete, give thanks for the gift of food and medicine and also to the surrounding plants and elements that supported the growth of the plant you harvested.

## Wild food to start with: easy to find and to prepare
### Check field guides for proper identification

| PLANT | HARVEST TIME | PART OR FORM USED | CULINARY USE | MEDICINAL PROPERTIES |
|---|---|---|---|---|
| **chickweed**<br>*Stellaria media* | fall, spring, early summer | leaves, tender stems, flowers | salad, pesto, soup | supports lymphatic system; cleanses blood; high in vitamins and minerals |
| **violet**<br>*Viola sororia* | spring, summer | leaves, tender stems, flowers | salad, sandwich topping, pesto, smoothie, herbal tea | supports lymphatic system; cleanses blood; high in vitamins and antioxidants |
| **dandelion**<br>*Taraxacum officinale* | young leaves: early spring roots: all year, but best in late fall | young leaves, flowers, roots | salad, pesto, sauté, herbal tea | liver and digestion tonic; rich in vitamins and minerals |
| **purple deadnettle**<br>*Lamium purpureum* | early- mid spring | leaves, tender stems, flowers | salad, smoothie, sauté | can reduce sensitivity to allergens and inhibit inflammation |
| **lamb's quarter**<br>*Chenopodium album*<br><br>*contains oxalic acid | later summer, early fall | leaves and other tender above ground parts | salad, sauté, soup, smoothie | supports digestion, high in iron, calcium, vitamin C |
| **wood sorrel**<br>*Oxalis stricta*<br><br>*contains oxalic acid | spring, summer | leaves, flowers, tender stems | salad, soups, sauces, beverage | relieves indigestion; high in iron, calcium, vitamin C |

# PRACTICE 23: **Retreating and Adventures in Nature**

The world stops—at least the human, time-bound world—and you enter into the timeless rhythm of Nature. When you enter into extended periods in Nature, you begin to rise with the sun and slow down as the day ends. Your hurried pace slows, and your posture shifts as you aren't carrying as much "weight" on your shoulders. You can literally feel your nervous system unwind during this extended reprieve from your full schedule. Have you ever experienced this on vacation in a natural setting?

With intentionality and awareness, a vacation or adventure in Nature becomes a pilgrimage for restoration, renewal, and personal transformation. Rather than just good stories and pictures to share with family and friends, these become life-changing experiences.

With the practices in this book, you cultivate inner stillness, present-moment awareness, and a deep connection with Nature and the unseen world. With these skills, any adventure, vacation, or retreat into Nature becomes an entry point into profound inner peace, contentment, clarity, and a felt sense of connection with all of life and beyond.

Intrigued by new sights, smells, sounds, and diversity, your senses wake up from the unconscious state of days of the same routine. With clear intention and creativity, camping, backpacking, or a rental cabin can be incredibly restorative, renewing, and enlivening. Remember, this is your retreat; the only thing you can get wrong is purposely distracting yourself from the present moment. On the pages that follow is a general outline to help you create and enhance your journey.

**Creating your experience:**

**1.** Technology-free or minimal usage when absolutely necessary is key. Even a good night call to those at home can pull you out of retreat mode. If this is necessary for you to be able to get away, then go ahead, but try not to check email or text messages. This also includes posting pictures and thoughts online. Do this when you return.

Trust me, truly going technology-free is one of the best gifts you can give yourself. Yes, it can be slightly uncomfortable at first, but is incredibly freeing to your mind and spirit. Phones are for emergencies only and to take pictures if you are so inclined. In addition, make sure to communicate to everyone that you will be technology-free.

One of the amazing benefits of retreating in Nature is to be fully unplugged for an extended period of time. Your nervous system will thank you.

**2.** Consciously choose whether you will go alone or with a group.

- Going with your family? Set achievable expectations for your experience. Can you carve out some attention to the beginning and end of your day? Bringing awareness to the present moment will go a long way.

- If you are creating a weekend away with friends, be clear with them on your intent, and make sure it is in alignment with theirs. Choose wisely who you create your experience with.

- Make sure someone knows where you are going and a rough itinerary, particularly if you are going solo.

**3.** What is your intention for this time away? Clearly stating this aligns the experience you are creating with your "why" behind taking this journey.

- To recover and restore after a stressful time?

- To connect with your family and Nature?

- To see a different part of the world and to truly take it all in and be transformed by the experience?

- To experience spiritual renewal?

- To challenge yourself physically, push your limits, and awaken the aliveness and vitality within you?

- To simply be and enjoy life without the distractions and trying to meet the needs of others?

**4.** Choose wisely what items you bring along on your journey. Traveling light can help you to feel unencumbered and uncluttered. Since this is a journey into Nature, you will feel more comfortable and safer with the proper gear. Plenty of people have started a hike on a beautiful sunny day and then had the weather turn quickly and risk hypothermia setting in. This is obviously something to consider in certain areas, like high mountains, more than in others (like the beach).

- Be sure you have done some homework about the weather conditions and hazards in the area you are going to so you are prepared. Also, make sure you have good footgear to match your conditions.

- A basic first-aid kit and plenty of water are always a must.

**5.** Food is an important part of your retreat. Make sure you are nourishing yourself with whole food. The eating with intention practice is perfect for mealtimes. With this retreat or adventure experience, you want to be as intentional as possible with each moment. Listen to your body, how it feels, and what you need.

You might even incorporate a period of fasting into this time if called to. Make sure what you are putting into your body is nourishing and in alignment with your intention.

**6.** Journal about how you are feeling now and reflect on how you want to feel at the end of this journey. Take your time with this writing practice; go deep. The clearer you are, the better able you will be to create the experience that you need.

- Align your journey to how you want to feel at the end.

- While planning your experience, ask yourself, "Will this help me to feel _____?" An honest answer will be a great navigational tool for this experience.

- For example, ask this question when choosing where you will sleep, who you choose to be with, or a specific activity you might be looking into.

**7.** Using your reflections and Nature as a guide, begin to create some intentionality and rhythm around your days.

## Waking up:

- Are you feeling drawn to rise with the sun or letting yourself wake up naturally? Your adventure might dictate this for you, so go with that.

- What is your intention for the day? This is connected to the overall intention you had for this journey. It might evolve daily as new awareness arises.

- Are there practices that you can do, such as yoga, tai chi, meditation, journaling, a Nature sit spot, or prayer, that support you and this intention? Make sure to create space first thing in the morning for this to happen.

## During the day:

- Try not to overfill it with things to do or expectations. Ideally, you have a rough idea, perhaps a hike or some Nature connection practices you would like to experience.

- Allow the day to unfold without controlling the flow of events. This allows for a host of divine synchronicities to guide you, which is usually exactly what you need to experience.

- Throughout the day, ask yourself, "Does this help me to feel _____?" which is related to your intention. If the answer is no, stop what you are doing and gently redirect yourself.

- Throughout the day, whether you are sea kayaking, hiking, or sitting on the porch, check to see where your attention is. Are you in the present moment, in connection with the life around you, or with your thoughts? Use the Body Practice to gently guide yourself back.

## Ending your day:

- Create the same intention to close your day as you started. Are you feeling drawn to end your day as the sun is going down? Do you want to be out star gazing?

- Try a journaling practice such as fluid journaling and write down all the synchronicities that happened during the day. Things might even come into your awareness that you didn't notice at the time. Don't filter, and just write for a minimum of five minutes.

- What other practices do you feel called to do to help you integrate your day?

- Right before you sleep, recall the moments you are grateful for that occurred during the day.

**IMPORTANT NOTE:**

As you unplug from the world, you will first feel relief, but without our everyday distractions, it can become uncomfortable. Unresolved issues that you have been ignoring or unexpressed feelings and emotions might rise to your awareness without all the distractions.

First, remember that Nature is healing, and you can ask for support in the challenge you are experiencing. If you stay with the feeling of what is coming up rather than mentally processing it, this can be a powerful healing experience.

Practice feeling what is uncomfortable and staying with it until it shifts. If tears well up, let them flow. If there is a sound you can make to help give voice to what you are experiencing, do that. Perhaps getting into some water would feel supportive (see chapter seven).

Allow your wisdom to guide you. Trust yourself. If something comes up that feels too big to handle on your own, use your senses and movement to let go of what arises and seek professional help after your journey.

## PRACTICE 24: **Guiding Kids in Nature**

Yes, this is actually a practice for you, the adult reading this! Allow the child in your life to remind you of the childlike wonder within, as you explore the natural world together. We enter into the world of exploration and discovery by dropping our agenda, letting go of time, and putting down our devices.

Children have a natural affinity for Nature. Put a group of children in the woods or on a beach, and they will start building forts, digging for treasures, creating castles, or tracking animals. As adults, thinking about these moments in childhood bring sweetness and can cause our bodies to relax.

There are several ways to support children in interacting with Nature, but one of the best practices is to simply get out of the way and follow the child. Let their curiosity lead you. Be it in the backyard, a local park, or a creek in the woods, their discoveries and play will be way more inspiring and authentic than we could ever come up with. You offer them the space, and let their imaginations run wild. You gift them by stepping back and they will gift you with their joy.

If this is new to the child or young person you are with, you can set the tone of ease and curiosity to get the exploration going. Then quietly step back as they begin to explore and create in their own ways. Your awareness and engagement with the present moment, comfort level with Nature, and curiosity will be a guidepost for them.

As the guide, how you respond to the natural world will speak volumes to the child. For example, you might have an issue with snakes. This is a great opportunity not to pass this fear on to a child and at the same time work on shifting your fear. Instead, learn about snakes, what types of snakes are in your area, when they are most active, where they like to hide, and what they want to eat.

Through your curiosity and learning about snakes, you develop respect for them and teach this to your young person.

When I'm leading groups of young people in the woods, I suggest not running but walking, and being curious about everything around. This helps everyone move slowly, so you see something as beautiful as a snake before you step on it. Assisting young people in developing awareness of their surroundings is a fantastic gift. Over time, they will observe things that most miss and make connections and creations that are authentic and unique.

This level of awareness also translates into other areas of life. After building Nature awareness with groups of young people, I have taken them to museums, and the feedback from the staff is often on how thoughtful, observant, and insightful they are. These are skills they have cultivated through their time being out in Nature. They learn to perceive what other children miss; through experiences in Nature, you are helping to nurture an amazing adult.

My husband and I started taking our daughter backpacking when she was three. She would have a little stuffed animal on her back; we hiked a mile, took our time, and set up camp. We kept it fun and gradually increased the experience until, by eleven years old, she hiked for two months on the Appalachian Trail along with her eight-year-old brother. We always keep it fun and make it an exploration, and these experiences have become part of them. Some might think you have to wait until they are older, but by the time they hit teenage years, it is actually harder to get them into the woods with parents or guardians. It can become a forced march, which I have witnessed before on the trail! Unless your family has been getting out together regularly as your child grows up or they are really interested, a teaser such as an adventure camp may be the hook they need to start exploring the natural world.

For youth and teens, their interactions with Nature will be different than with a child. At this age, they are starting to want to take more risks. Giving your young person an experience of the perceived risk out in Nature can be powerful for their personal development. Overcoming a fear of heights through rock climbing, jumping into a cold creek, or even a night of camping in the woods offers points of challenge. When inviting young people to challenge their edges, that point where they start to feel uncomfortable, always frame it as an invitation, a "challenge by choice." Keep inviting them to cross over that edge, as eventually, they will, and they will do it on their terms. When it's fully their choice, meeting a challenge is incredibly empowering.

When I lead groups of teens into the woods, I hire reputable guide services for activities such as rock climbing. Do your homework and look for recommendations. In addition, learning about survival skills or taking a class with your young person can be a great way to connect with them and inspire explorations in Nature.

It is important to be aware that even a hike can go dangerously wrong if you are not prepared. Take your time to fully prepare—research the challenges and weather variations of the area you are going to, pack a basic first aid kit, plenty of water, snacks, and layers of weather protection. Also, don't forget to let a trusted person know where you are going and how long you plan to be gone.

For all age groups, foraging is magical. Kids love to find food and eat it! This forms a powerful bond between the earth and a child. They make an important realization about how the earth is nourishing to us, and this instills gratitude for Nature. This is a great hobby to start with a young person in your life. Refer to the practice of Foraging (chapter eleven).

When I teach children about foraging, they will hear me repeatedly say never to eat anything unless it has been seen and approved by a knowledgeable adult. Include this reminder while at the same time teaching them the identifying characteristics of the plants they are foraging. Eventually, they will become the expert.

Cultivating a connection with Nature as a young person is profound. They will grow to love, respect, have the desire to protect Nature, and the awareness to go out to Nature for restoration and healing as an adult. This is a life-changing gift.

CONCLUSION

# welcome home

"The care of the earth is our most ancient and most worthy, and after all, our most pleasing responsibility. To cherish what remains of it and to foster its renewal is our only legitimate hope."

—WENDELL BERRY

We have the honor of tending to two homes, both of which have been harmed after years of neglect and misuse—our body and the earth. Nature brings us hope, and we are the hope of Nature.

In the midst of our overstimulated world, many of us are being called to seek a simpler way of being. The simpler path is often closer to the natural world and gentler to the earth. We don't have to change things overnight—that would not be wise or sustainable—but we are all being called to take one simple step after the next. When done consistently and over time, the simplest actions can be the most transformational ones.

This journey is slow and gentle, but it has the power to transform your life completely. With Nature as your guide, you will experience restoration of the nervous system, calmness and clarity of mind, and peacefulness of heart. This is how we heal and can help heal the earth.

This is the journey of coming **home** to ourselves.

......................................................................................................

......................................................................................................

......................................................................................................

......................................................................................................

......................................................................................................

......................................................................................................

......................................................................................................

......................................................................................................

......................................................................................................

......................................................................................................

......................................................................................................

......................................................................................................

......................................................................................................

......................................................................................................

FIELD NOTES

# ACKNOWLEDGMENTS

All of creation is an interconnected tapestry whose focus is to bring forth new life. This book is one little offering of new life, hopefully, a fresh perspective. Each thread of its fabric is from all the amazing people that have been part of my life, those whose footsteps I follow, and all the landscapes I have been fortunate enough to roam and be a part of. With this acknowledgment, I'll make a feeble attempt to highlight some of the "threads" that have been instrumental to the creation of this book, and without them, this wouldn't have happened.

So much of this book is infused with the concept of grounding and landing in your body. No one can do this work for you, but there are those in your life that can help provide an anchor for you to do your work. My anchor has been Greg. With unending patience and love, you have gifted me the freedom to unfurl more deeply into myself; I am forever grateful to you.

To my parents, John and Bette, who have always supported me in dreaming big. You have always been a safety net of unending kindness, love, and generosity. And to Marge and Neal for your steadfast love, support, and encouragement.

To Marianne, my twin, you've been my fierce protector, unabashedly honest, unwavering supporter, and given me unending love.

Two of my greatest teachers in the world have been my children, Gracie and Andrew. In many ways, I grew up with them. They inspire me, challenge me to grow as a human, and teach me how to love more deeply. Your courage, brilliance, and creativity make me one proud mama.

To Cinnamon Kennedy, you brought structure and life to this book, and Paula Gross, you speak the words of Nature and my heart; your thoughtfulness in editing was invaluable. I can't imagine putting this book into the world without the two of you.

Erica de Flamand, you bring beauty to all you do, this book included—I am very grateful for your inspired cover and interior design. And gratitude to Andrea Jasmin, whose kindness and expertise with proofreading and editorial support have helped bring this offering to the world.

To my beloved friends who have read and helped mold the different versions of this book into being, who have supported me in living out the content of this book, and who have loved me into a greater sense of belonging, thank you, Cindy, Kelly, Julia, Lisa, and Phil.

To all the staff and children from the Davidson Green school, from the Golden 8 to the present—you all inspire me as we have worked to create a more sustainable future, and you've gifted me great joy as we have experienced Nature together for the past eleven years. A special thank you to my dear friend and co-creator, Jennifer Jakubecy, who wooed me into creating a school—I am very grateful you did, as what we created is beautiful, and the lessons I have learned are invaluable.

To Wendy, my dear friend and retreat co-creator extraordinaire, it's through creating experiences with you that I have been able to step deeply into the healing power of Nature.

To all the amazing souls who have been reading my articles over the years and attending my retreats, thank you!! You all have inspired me to keep going and to write this book.

I have teachers along the way, both in the classroom and in life, who have helped and supported the unfolding and unfurling of me. I'm beyond grateful to Helen Yamada, Larry Morris, Doug Silsbee, Lynn Erickson, Robin Rose Bennett, and Roy Alexander. You are the elders that I had searched for and fortunately found.

## APPENDIX A: **Tips on Gardening**

There is a reason we have so many gardening metaphors for life. It is an engaging adventure full of trial and error, but one where you receive the benefits of Nature connection, whether you produce a bumper yield or not. Make a commitment to grow anything you are interested in. There are countless resources on gardening, but one of my favorites is Toby Hemenway's book, *Gaia's Garden*. Below are my distilled tips to help you get started growing.

**What type of plants are you interested in growing?**
- plants that benefit pollinators
- culinary herbs
- medicinal herbs (often herbs that benefit us benefit the pollinators as well)
- an edible landscape, such as berry bushes and fruit trees
- food—vegetable plants do best when interplanted with aromatic herbs (such as those in the Practice 18 chart). Many herbs help deter garden pests.
- tough, resilient plants for beginners—many culinary and medical herbs are incredibly resilient, making them great plants to start with.

**Location: What locations are available to you?**
Plants' needs are tied to sunlight exposure, so this is your first consideration. After that, location is more about what works for you to provide care and easy access.
- Most herbs and vegetable plants need full sun - at least five-six hours of direct sunlight.
- As long as you have enough light, you can grow plants in window boxes, containers on patios, or in garden beds.
- If growing herbs or vegetables, locate your garden as close to your kitchen door as possible. This placement will enhance your connection with your garden, as it will inspire you to harvest fresh herbs to cook with and notice if there are pests or if your plants are drying out.

- If you are growing in containers, set them away from your house in the summer to prevent them from drying out too quickly. Materials such as brick hold heat (think thermal mass) which can become too much for the summer. In cooler weather, however, move them closer, as the thermal mass can help extend your growing season.
- If you live in an old house that might have had lead paint, set your edible or medicinal garden further away from your home.
- Look out for neighboring pesticide or herbicide use. If you are downslope from your neighbors, when it rains, whatever is on their grass will end up on your property. If this is the case, try to locate your garden away from this runoff or plant a buffer of ornamental plants to slow the flow of water.
- Community gardens are a great option for those without enough sunlight or space.

**Water considerations:**
- You need access to water.
- If you are growing in containers, they will dry out much quicker than planting in the ground. During the summer, they may need watering every day or every other day.
- A layer of mulch around all your plants and even in your containers can conserve a significant amount of water. Compost, wheat straw, and dried leaves work well for mulching.

**Soil:**
- Soil is the foundation. Without nutrient-rich soil, you will not have healthy plants. If plants are healthy, they will be more resilient to pests. The best way to add the full range of nutrients to your soil is through compost and other organic matter, such as decayed leaves. Feed your soil, and it will feed you!
- If you are planting in containers, you can purchase premade potting soil or easily make your own.

Do not fill containers with native soil (soil that you dug up); it behaves differently in containers and won't drain well enough. There are many recipes online for creating well-draining, nutrient-rich potting soil for containers.

- For creating a new garden bed, techniques such as lasagna gardening or sheet mulching are excellent strategies for creating healthy soil. These methods just require planning ahead a season (the first time only). Gaia's Garden has a lot of great information on building nutrient-rich and living soil.

**Plants:**

- Read about the needs of the plants you are interested in growing. What are their light and space requirements? For example, make sure your taller plants, such as tomatoes, don't overshadow smaller plants in your garden bed or container. Look how the sun is traveling across the sky. If your garden bed is aligned from east to west, you will plant taller plants on the north side of the bed.
- Planting calendars are great tools to help you plan your garden. You can find these in local garden shops and online. Most state extension services have online planting calendars that tell you the best time of year to start specific food plants. This changes from region to region, so be sure you look for a planting chart specific to yours.
- In the Southeast, fruit trees and bushes tend to get the best start when planted in the fall.

THE NATURE RESET

...........................................................................................................

...........................................................................................................

...........................................................................................................

...........................................................................................................

...........................................................................................................

...........................................................................................................

...........................................................................................................

...........................................................................................................

...........................................................................................................

...........................................................................................................

...........................................................................................................

...........................................................................................................

...........................................................................................................

 FIELD NOTES

# NOTES

## Introduction

1. Theodore Roszak, "Where Psyche Meets Gaia," essay, in Ecopsychology: Restoring the Earth, healing the mind (San Francisco: Sierra Club Books, 1995), 1–17.

## Chapter 1

1. MaryCarol R. Hunter, Brenda W. Gillespie, and Sophie Yu-Pu Chen, "Urban Nature Experiences Reduce Stress in the Context of Daily Life Based on Salivary Biomarkers," Frontiers in Psychology 10 (2019), https://doi.org/10.3389/fpsyg.2019.00722.

2. Jo Barton and Jules Pretty, "What Is the Best Dose of Nature and Green Exercise for Improving Mental Health? A Multi-Study Analysis," Environmental Science & Technology 44, no. 10 (2010): 3947–55, https://doi.org/10.1021/es903183r.

3. Li, Qing. 2010. "Effect of Forest Bathing Trips on Human Immune Function." Environmental Health and Preventive Medicine 15 (1): 9–17. https://doi.org/10.1007/s12199-008-0068-3.

4. Kabat-Zinn, Jon. 2005. Wherever You Go, There You Are: Mindfulness Meditation in Everyday Life. USA: Hachette Books.

## Chapter 2

1. "Stress symptoms: Effects on your body and behavior." 2023. Mayo Clinic. https://www.mayoclinic.org/healthy-lifestyle/stress-management/in-depth/stress-symptoms/art-20050987.

2. Levine, Peter A. 1997. Waking The Tiger. Berkeley, CA: North Atlantic Books.

3. Van der Kolk, Bessel A. 2015. *The Body Keeps the Score: Mind, Brain and Body in the Transformation of Trauma.* Harlow, England: Penguin Books.

4. Louv, Richard. 2006. *Last Child in the Woods: Saving Our Children from Nature-Deficit Disorder.* Algonquin Books.

## Chapter 3

1. Csikszentmihalyi, Mihaly. 2008. *Flow: The Psychology of Optimal Experience.* New York, NY: HarperPerennial.

2. Levine, Peter A. 1997. *Waking The Tiger.* Berkeley, CA: North Atlantic Books.

3. Delio, Ilia. 2013. *The Unbearable Wholeness of Being: God, Evolution and the Power of Love.* Maryknoll, NY: Orbis Books.

4. Saint-Exupéry, Antoine de. 2023. *The Little Prince.* London, England: HarperCollins.

## Chapter 4

1. "Why Sleep Matters: Consequences of Sleep Deficiency | Sleep Medicine." 21. Division of Sleep Medicine at Harvard Medical School. https://sleep.hms.harvard.edu/education-training/public-education/sleep-and-health-education-program/sleep-health-education-45. Retrieved from http://healthysleep.med.harvard.edu/healthy/matters/consequences.

# BIBLIOGRAPHY

Ackerman, Diane. *A Natural History of the Senses.* New York, NY: Vintage Books, 1992.

Alfs, Matthew. *300 Herbs: Their Indications and Their Contraindications.* London, England: Aeon Books, 2022.

Alvarsson, Jesper J., Stefan Wiens, and Mats E. Nilsson. "Stress Recovery during Exposure to Nature Sound and Environmental Noise." *International Journal of Environmental Research and Public Health* 7, no. 3 (2010): 1036–46. https://doi.org/10.3390/ijerph7031036.

Annerstedt, Matilda, and Peter Währborg. "Nature-Assisted Therapy: Systematic Review of Controlled and Observational Studies." *Scandinavian Journal of Public Health* 39, no. 4 (2011): 371–88. https://doi.org/10.1177/1403494810396400.

Bennett, Robin Rose. *Healing Magic: A Green Witch Guidebook to Conscious Living.* Gaia Rose Publishing, 2014.

———. *The Gift of Healing Herbs.* Berkeley, CA: North Atlantic Books, 2014.

Berman, Marc G., John Jonides, and Stephen Kaplan. "The Cognitive Benefits of Interacting with Nature." *Psychological Science* 19, no. 12 (2008): 1207–12. https://doi.org/10.1111/j.1467-9280.2008.02225.x.

Bringslimark, Tina, Terry Hartig, and Grete G. Patil. "The Psychological Benefits of Indoor Plants: A Critical Review of the Experimental Literature." *Journal of Environmental Psychology* 29, no. 4 (2009): 422–33. https://doi.org/10.1016/j.jenvp.2009.05.001.

Cohen, Michael. *Reconnecting with Nature: Finding Wellness Through Restoring Your Bond with the Earth.* Ecopress, 1997.

Cox, Daniel, Danielle Shanahan, Hannah Hudson, Richard Fuller, Karen Anderson, Steven Hancock, and Kevin Gaston. "Doses of Nearby Nature Simultaneously Associated with Multiple Health Benefits." *International Journal of Environmental Research and Public Health* 14 no. 2 (2017): 172. https://doi.org/10.3390/ijerph14020172.

Cox, Daniel T. C., Danielle F. Shanahan, Hannah L. Hudson, Kate E. Plummer, Gavin M. Siriwardena, Richard A. Fuller, Karen Anderson, Steven Hancock, and Kevin J. Gaston. "Doses of Neighborhood Nature: The Benefits for Mental Health of Living with Nature." *Bioscience.* (2017). https://doi.org/10.1093/biosci/biw173.

Fuller, Richard A., Katherine N. Irvine, Patrick Devine-Wright, Philip H. Warren, and Kevin J. Gaston. "Psychological Benefits of Greenspace Increase with Biodiversity." Biology Letters 3, no. 4 (2007): 390–94. https://doi.org/10.1098/rsbl.2007.0149.

Gladstar, Rosemary. Herbs for Reducing Stress & Anxiety. North Adams, MA: Storey Books, 1999.

Hanh, Thich Nhat. The Miracle of Mindfulness: An Introduction to the Practice of Meditaion. Boston, MA: Beacon Press, 1999.

———. Peace Is Every Step: The Path of Mindfulness in Everyday Life. Shambhala Publications, 2009.

Hartung, Tammi. Homegrown Herbs a Complete Guide to Growing, Using, and Enjoying More than 100 Herbs. North Adams, MA: Storey Publishing, 2011.

Hemenway, Toby. Gaia's Garden: A Guide to Home-Scale Permaculture - 2nd Edition. 2nd ed. White River Junction, VT: Chelsea Green Publishing, 2009.

Hoffmann, David. The New Holistic Herbal. 3rd ed. London, England: Thorsons, 1994.

Kabat-Zinn, Jon. Coming to Our Senses: Healing Ourselves and the World through Mindfulness. London, England: Piatkus Books, 2005.

Kallas, John. Edible Wild Plants: Wild Foods from Dirt to Plate. Layton, UT: Gibbs M. Smith, 2010.

Kaplan, Stephen. "The Restorative Benefits of Nature: Toward an Integrative Framework." Journal of Environmental Psychology 15, no. 3 (1995): 169–82. https://doi.org/10.1016/0272-4944(95)90001-2.

Lee, Kate E., Kathryn J. H. Williams, Leisa D. Sargent, Nicholas S. G. Williams, and Katherine A. Johnson. "40-Second Green Roof Views Sustain Attention: The Role of Micro-Breaks in Attention Restoration." Journal of Environmental Psychology 42: (2015). 182–89. https://doi.org/10.1016/j.jenvp.2015.04.003.

Leslie, Clare Walker. Keeping a Nature Journal, 3rd Edition: Deepen Your Connection with the Natural World All around You. North Adams, MA: Storey Publishing, 2021.

Louv, Richard. The Nature Principle: Reconnecting with Life in a Virtual Age. Algonquin Books, 2012.

McClintock, Clayton H. "Opening the Heart: A Spirituality of Gratitude." *Spirituality in Clinical Practice* (Washington, D.C.) 2, no. 1 (2015): 21–22. https://doi.org/10.1037/scp0000060.

Morita, Emi, Makoto Imai, Masako Okawa, Tomiyasu Miyaura, and Soichiro Miyazaki. "A before and after Comparison of the Effects of Forest Walking on the Sleep of a Community-Based Sample of People with Sleep Complaints." *BioPsychoSocial Medicine* 5, no. 1 (2011): 13. https://doi.org/10.1186/1751-0759-5-13.

Selhub, Eva M., and Alan C. Logan. *Your Brain on Nature: The Science of Nature's Influence on Your Health, Happiness, and Vitality.* Collins, 2014.

Shanahan, Danielle F., Richard A. Fuller, Robert Bush, Brenda B. Lin, and Kevin J. Gaston. "The Health Benefits of Urban Nature: How Much Do We Need?" *Bioscience* 65, no. 5 (2015): 476–85. https://doi.org/10.1093/biosci/biv032.

Silsbee, Doug. *Presence-Based Coaching: Cultivating Self-Generative Leaders through Mind, Body, and Heart.* 1st ed. Chichester, England: Jossey Bass Wiley, 2008.

Ulrich, R. S. "View through a Window May Influence Recovery from Surgery." *Science* (New York, N.Y.) 224, n0. 4647 (1984): 420–21. https://doi.org/10.1126/science.6143402.

Völker, Sebastian, and Thomas Kistemann. "The Impact of Blue Space on Human Health and Well-Being - Salutogenetic Health Effects of Inland Surface Waters: A Review." *International Journal of Hygiene and Environmental Health* 214 no. 6 (2011): 449–60. https://doi.org/10.1016/j.ijheh.2011.05.001.

Williams, Florence. *The Nature Fix: Why Nature Makes Us Happier, Healthier, and More Creative.* New York, NY: WW Norton, 2018.

Wilson, Edward O. *Biophilia.* London, England: Harvard University Press, 1984.

Winston, David, and Steven Maimes. *Adaptogens: Herbs for Strength Stamina and Stress Relief.* Rochester, NY: Healing Arts Press, 2007.

## ABOUT THE AUTHOR

Kathleen McIntyre, forest ecologist turned nature therapist, has been leading therapeutic and life-enriching experiences in Nature for the past 25 years. After receiving a Master's in Forest Resources, she began fusing her passion and knowledge of land conservation and restoration with Nature's wisdom teachings for profound personal healing and transformation.

When working with clients, groups, or leading retreats, Kathleen incorporates the science of somatic therapy, nature therapy, and mindfulness into a healing modality that leads to sustainable, long-term restoration of the nervous system and mental clarity, reclamation of the body, and reawakening of the spirit.

Kathleen lives in Davidson, North Carolina, where she co-founded the Davidson Green School and is the Director of Mindfulness and Outdoor Leadership. She is also a co-founder of NatureSoma.com – an online resource and community to support individuals in receiving the therapeutic benefits of Nature connection and to inspire action to protect and nurture the landscape they are part of.

katmcintyre.com

..........................................................................................................

..........................................................................................................

..........................................................................................................

..........................................................................................................

..........................................................................................................

..........................................................................................................

..........................................................................................................

..........................................................................................................

..........................................................................................................

..........................................................................................................

..........................................................................................................

..........................................................................................................

..........................................................................................................

  ..........................................................................

..........................................................................

FIELD NOTES

THE NATURE RESET

 FIELD NOTES